the best of
acoustic chill

Wise Publications
part of The Music Sales Group

London / New York / Paris / Sydney / Copenhagen / Berlin / Madrid / Tokyo

Published by
Wise Publications
8/9 Frith Street, London, W1D 3JB, England.

Exclusive distributors:
Music Sales Limited
Distribution Centre, Newmarket Road,
Bury St Edmunds, Suffolk, IP33 3YB, England.

Music Sales Pty Limited
120 Rothschild Avenue, Rosebery,
NSW 2018, Australia.

Order No. AM983081
ISBN 1-84609-097-0
This book © Copyright 2005 Wise Publications,
a division of Music Sales Limited.

Music processed by Paul Ewers Music Design.
Cover photograph courtesy of Photolibrary.

Printed in the United Kingdom.

www.musicsales.com

cinder and smoke

Words & Music by Samuel Beam

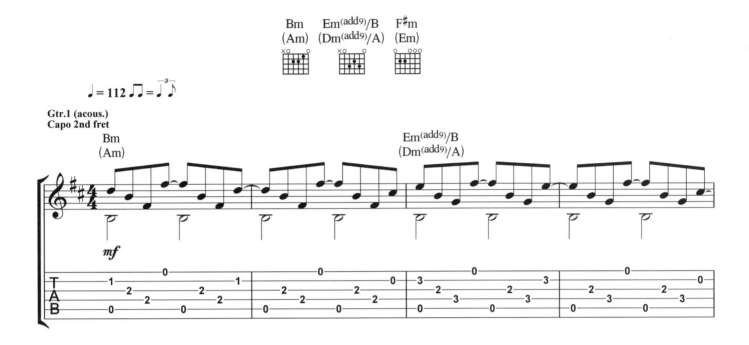

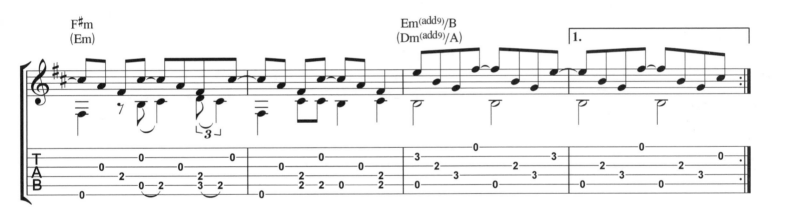

gar - den row____ is cov - ered in mud,
will____ to - night. I'll give it as fast,
drunk____ as all the fire - men shake____

and drag - ging your mo - - - - - ther's clothes.
and high as the____ flame____ will rise.
a pho - to from____ fa - - - ther's arms.

Cin - der and smoke,__ the snake in the__
Cin - der and smoke,__ some whis - pers a -
Cin - der and smoke,__ you'll ask me to

at the hop

Words & Music by Devendra Banhart

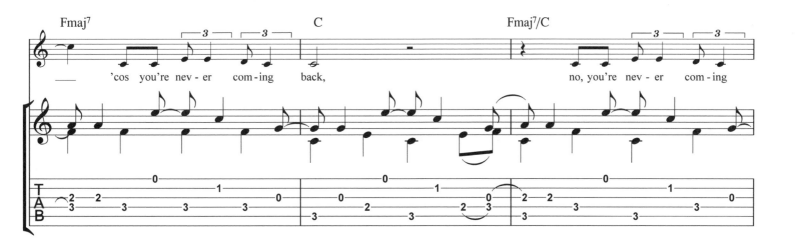

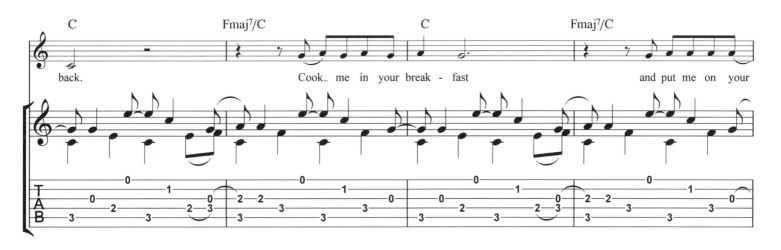

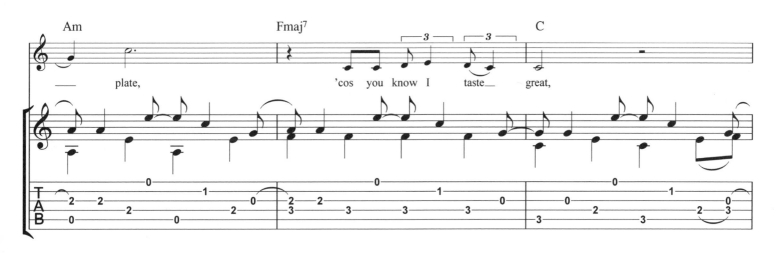

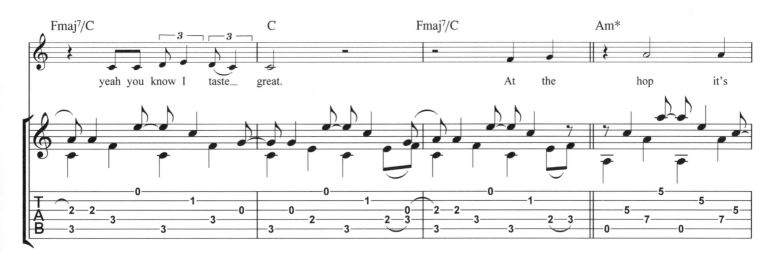

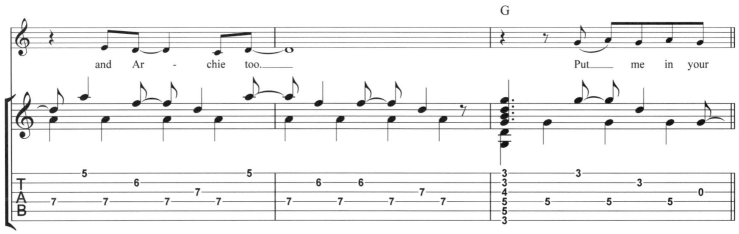

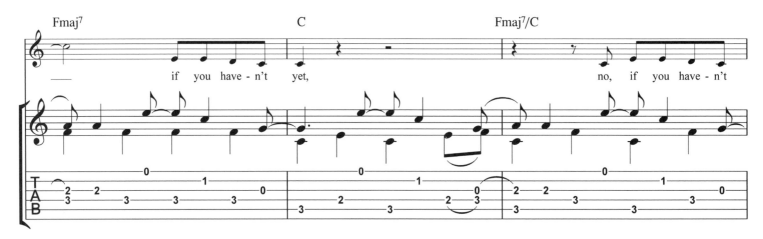

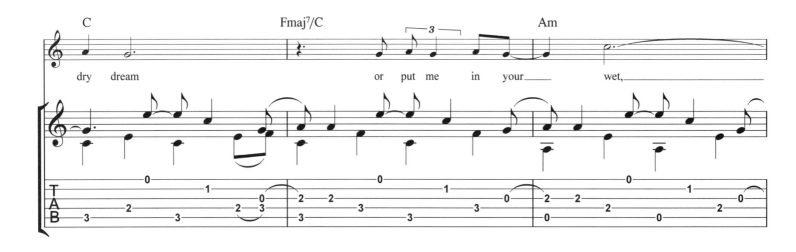

Light___ me with your can - dle

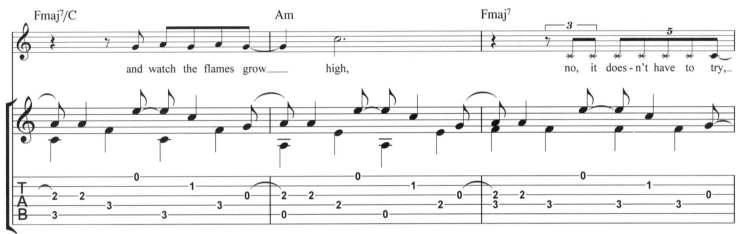

and watch the flames grow___ high, no, it does-n't have to try,___

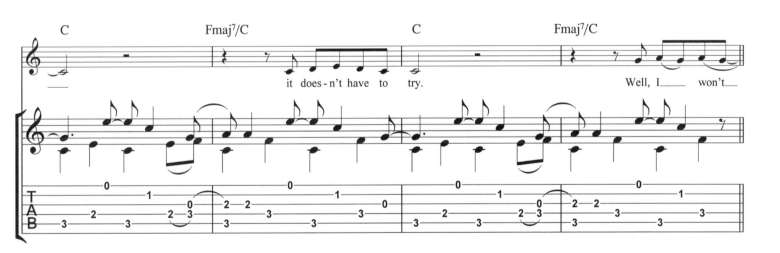

it does - n't have to try. Well, I___ won't___

___ stop all of my___ pre - tend - ing that you'll come

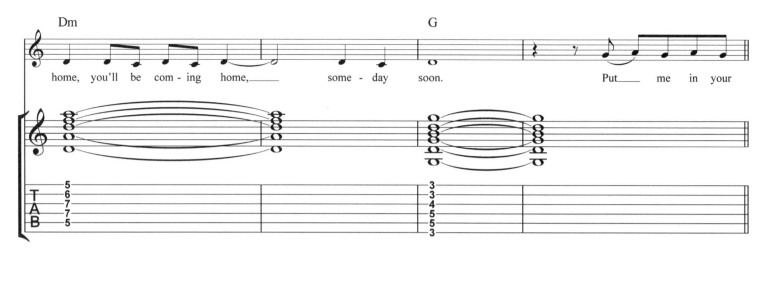

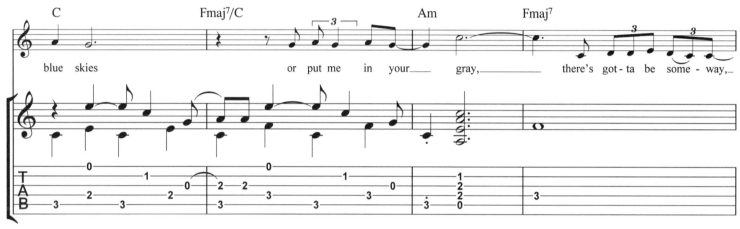

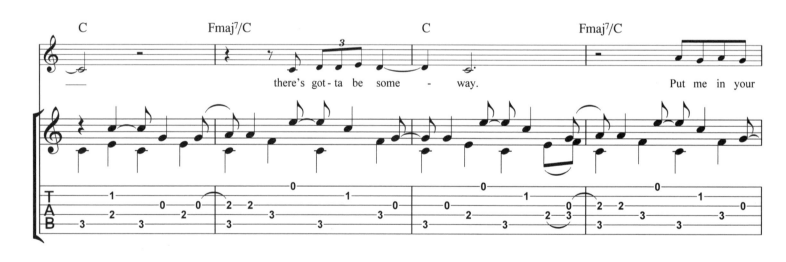

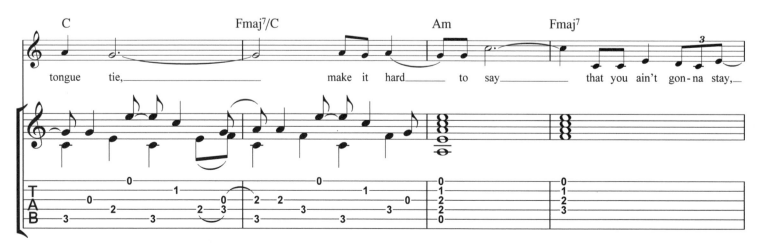

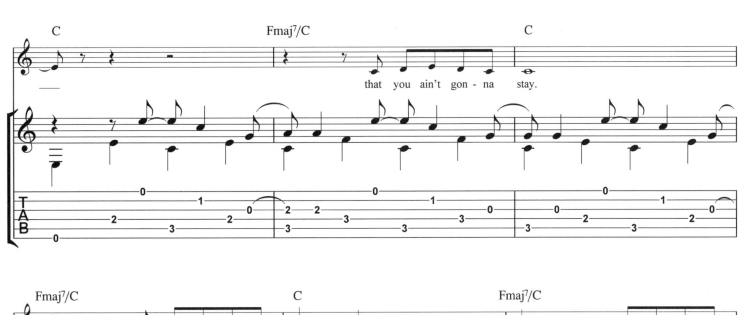

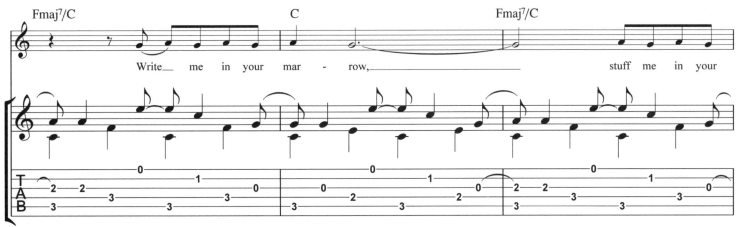

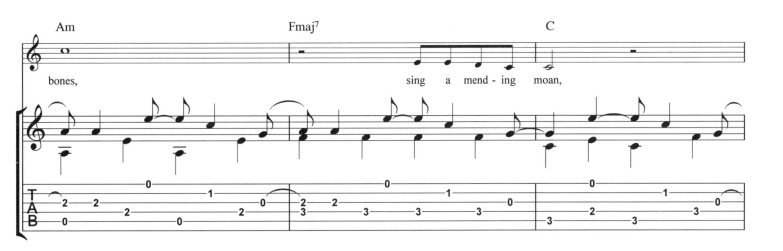

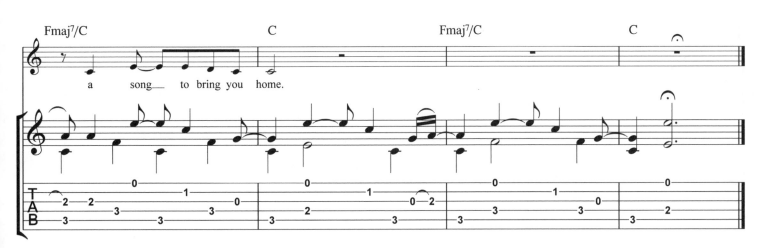

don't let go

Words & Music by Tom Baxter

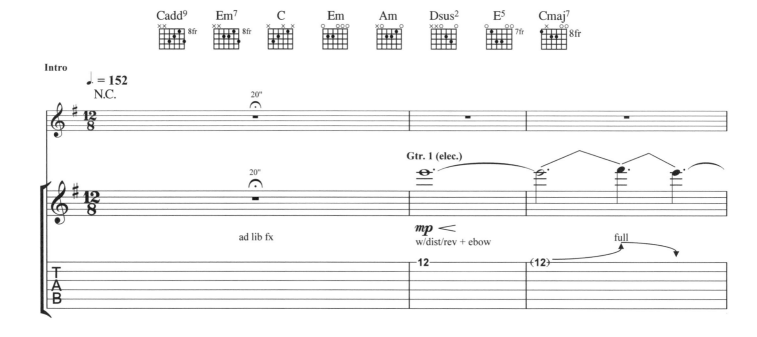

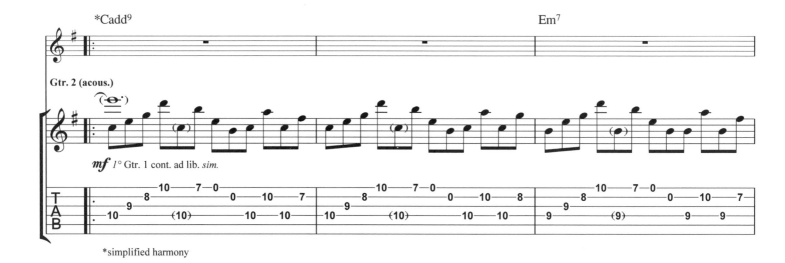

*simplified harmony

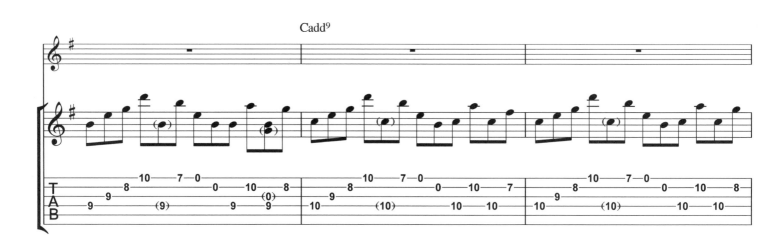

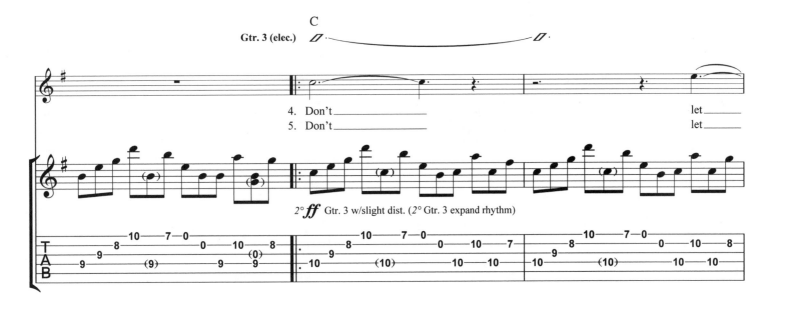

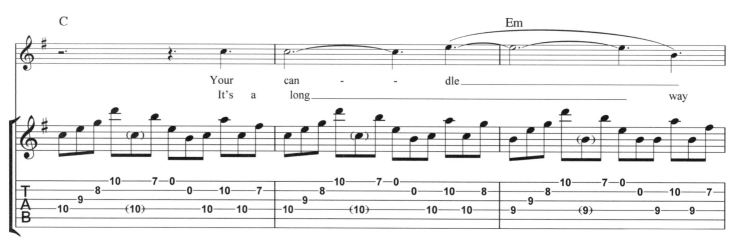

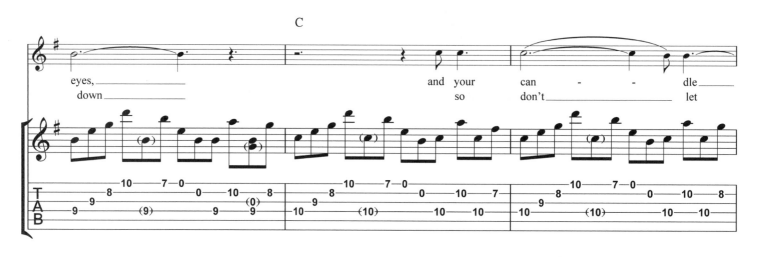

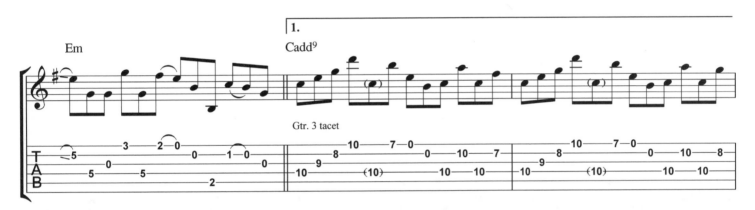

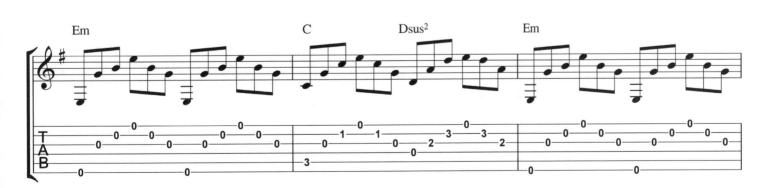

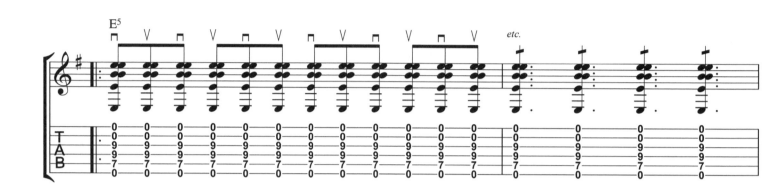

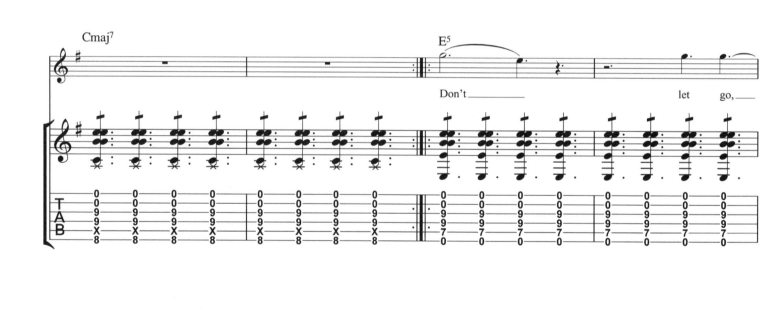

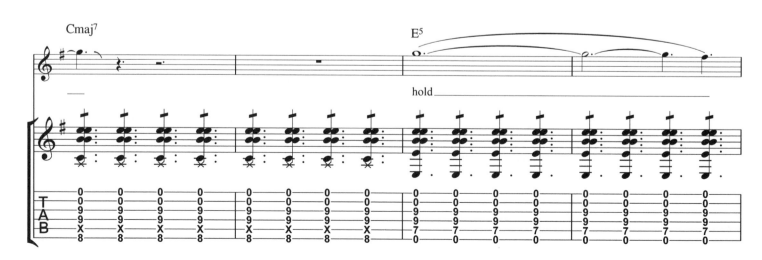

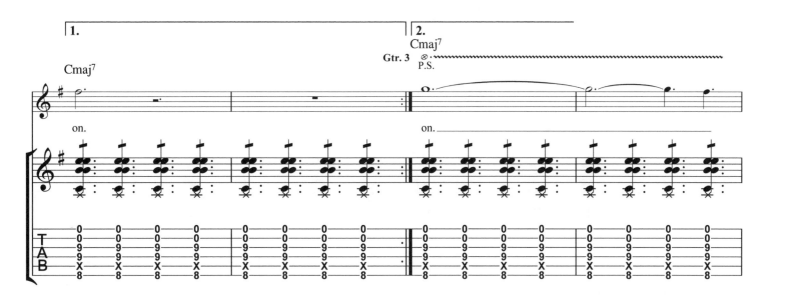

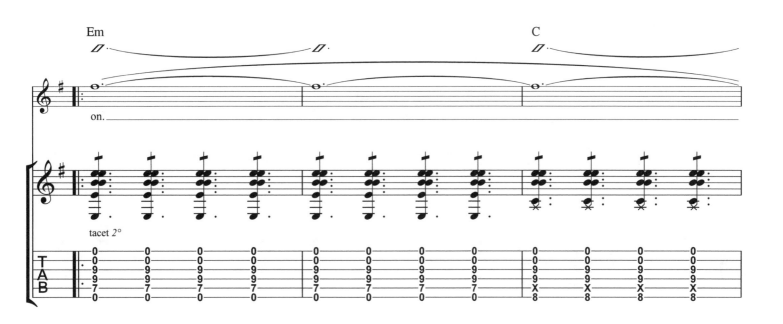

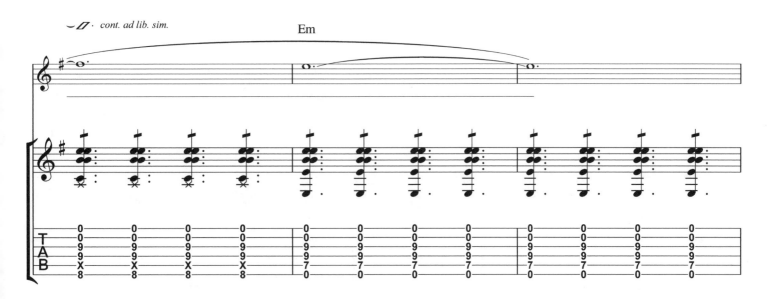

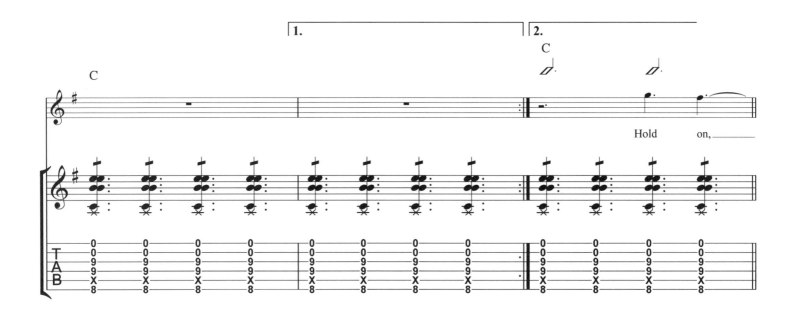

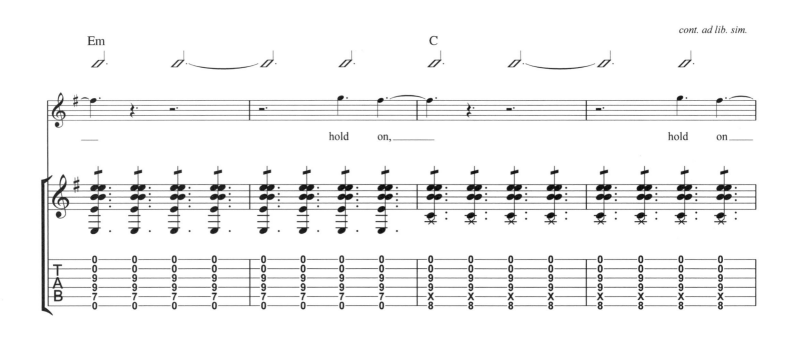

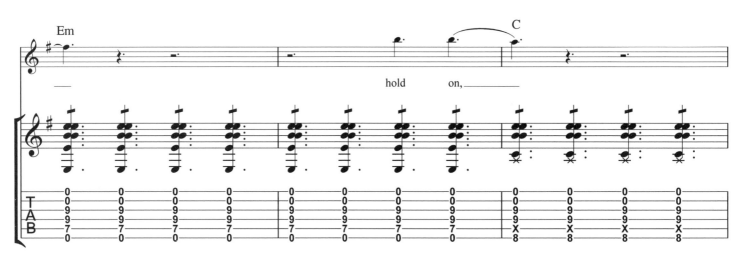

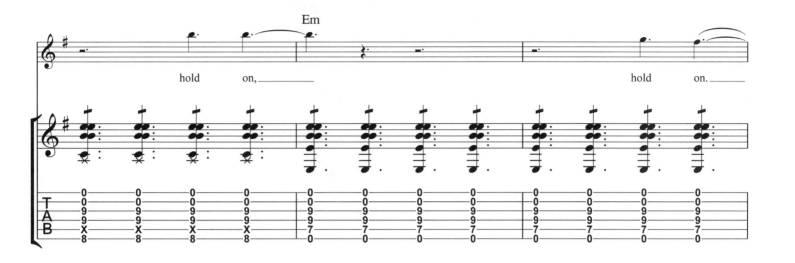

hold on,_____ hold on._____

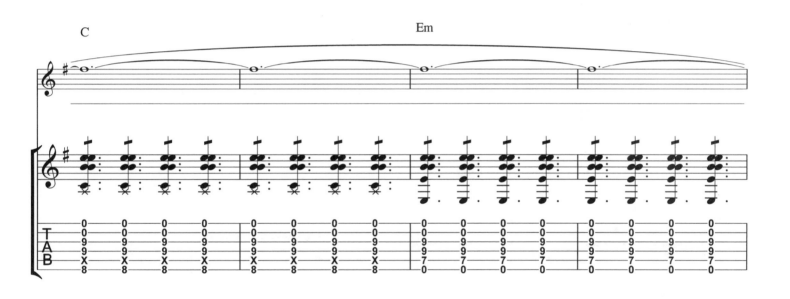

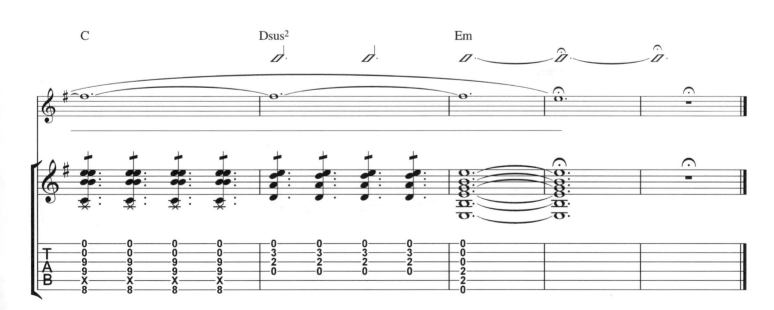

daughters

Words & Music by John Mayer

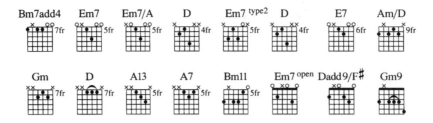

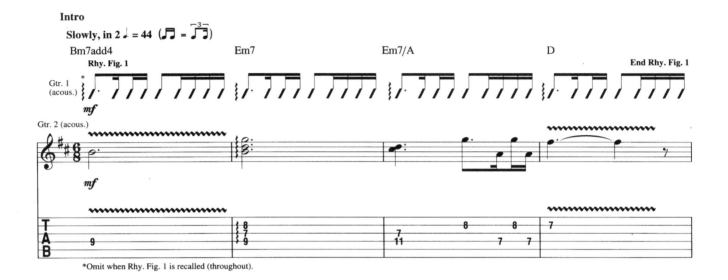

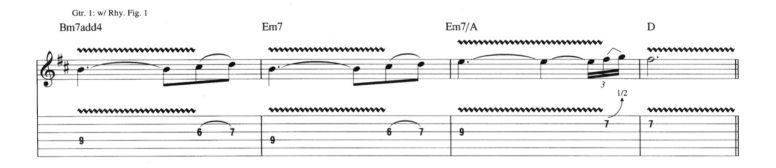

*Omit when Rhy. Fig. 1 is recalled (throughout).

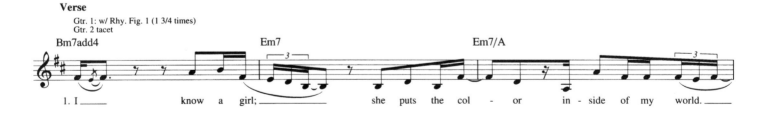

Verse

1. I ___ know a girl; she puts the col - or in - side of my world. ___

___ But she's just like a maze ___ where all of the walls ___

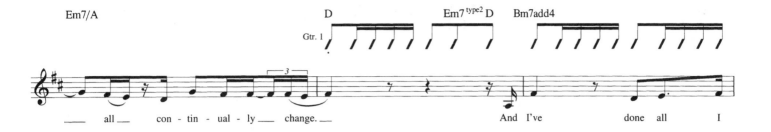

_____ all __ con - tin - ual - ly ____ change. ____ And I've done all I

can to stand on her steps __ with my heart in my hand. _____ Now

I'm start - ing to see may - be it's __ got __ noth - ing to do with me. _____

𝄋 **Chorus**
2nd & 3rd times, Bkgd. Voc.: w/ Voc. Fig. 1 (4 times)

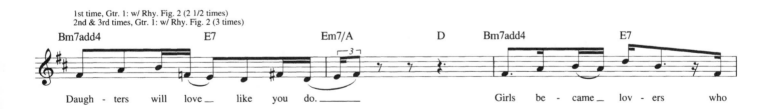

____ Fa - thers, be good __ to your daugh - ters.

1st time, Gtr. 1: w/ Rhy. Fig. 2 (2 1/2 times)
2nd & 3rd times, Gtr. 1: w/ Rhy. Fig. 2 (3 times)

Daugh - ters will love __ like you do. _____ Girls be - came __ lov - ers who

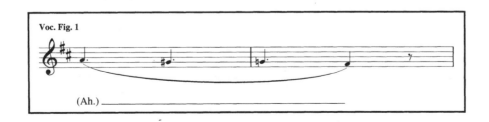

(Ah.) _____

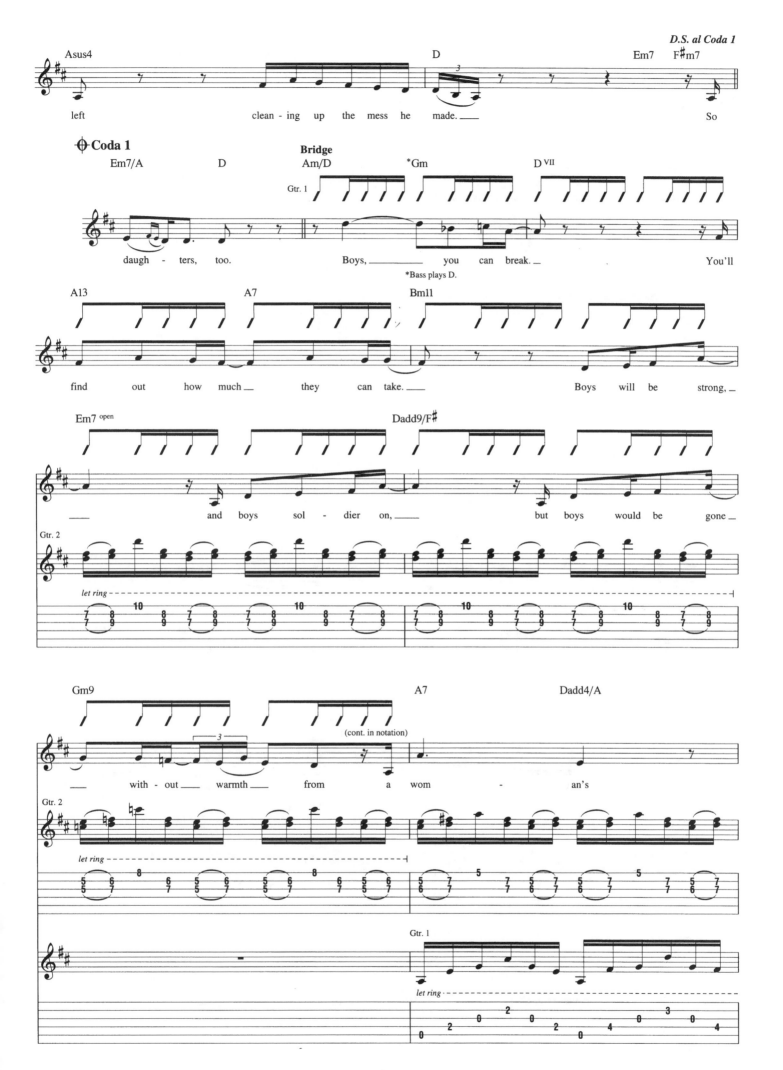

emily

Words & Music by Stephen Fretwell

32

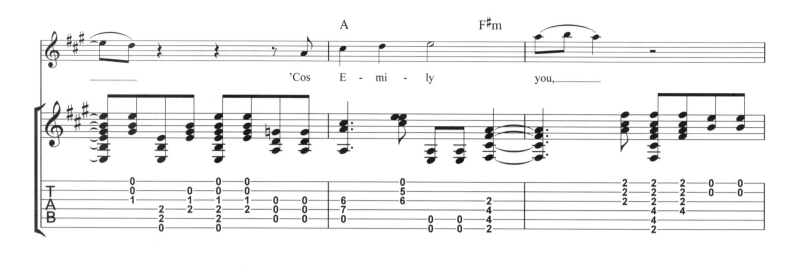

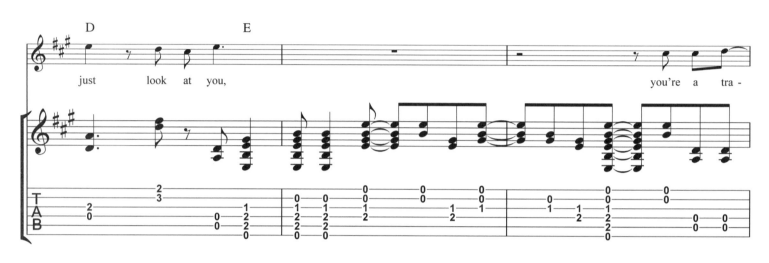

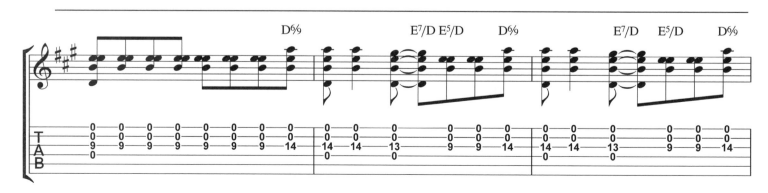

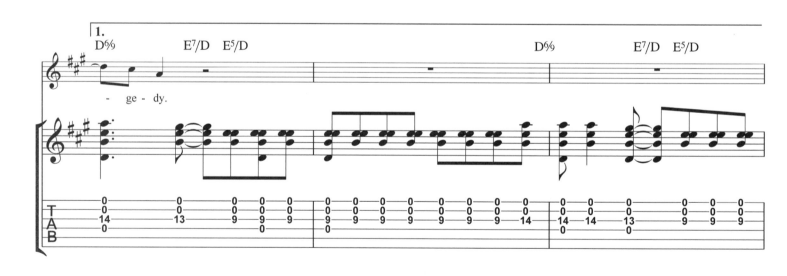

first day of my life

Words & Music by Conor Oberst

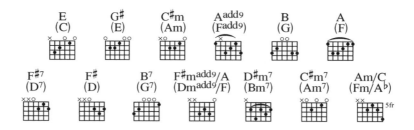

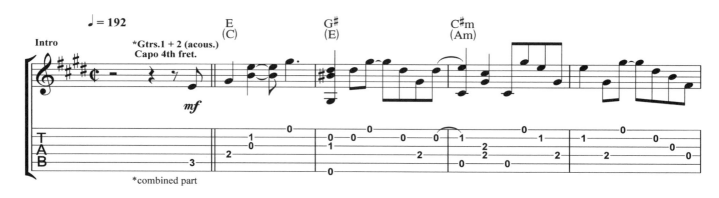

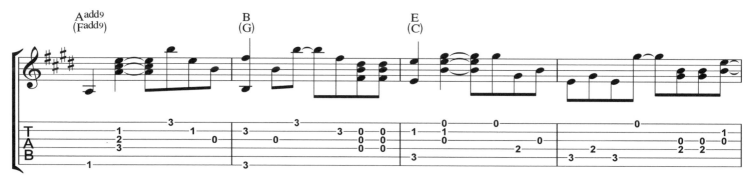

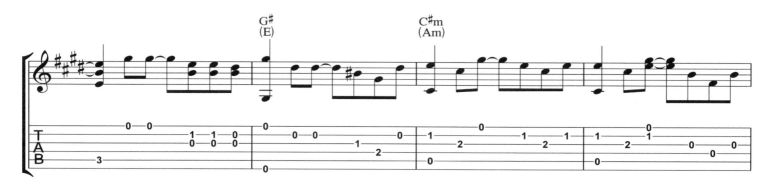

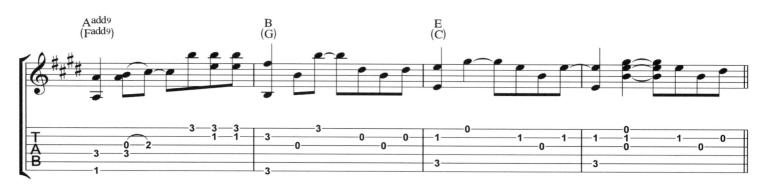

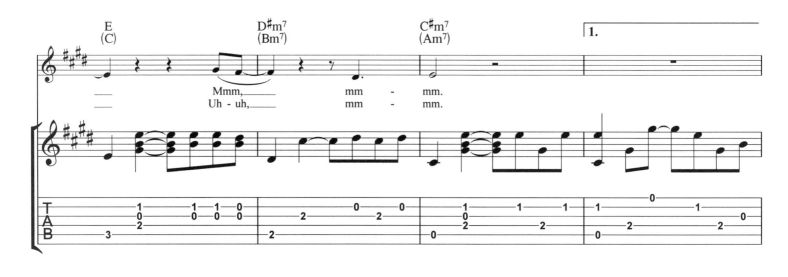

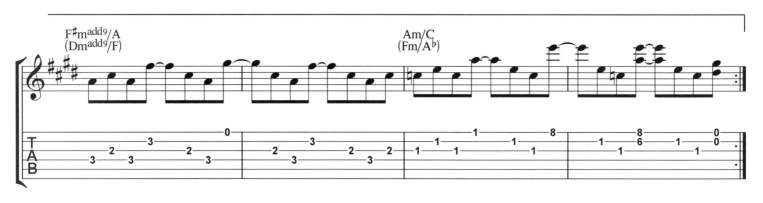

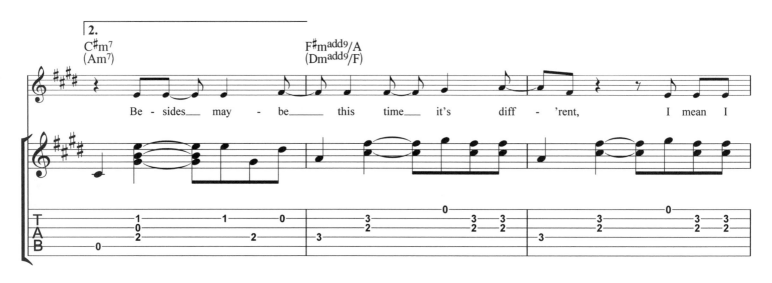

hold you in my arms

Words & Music by Ray LaMontagne & Ethan Johns

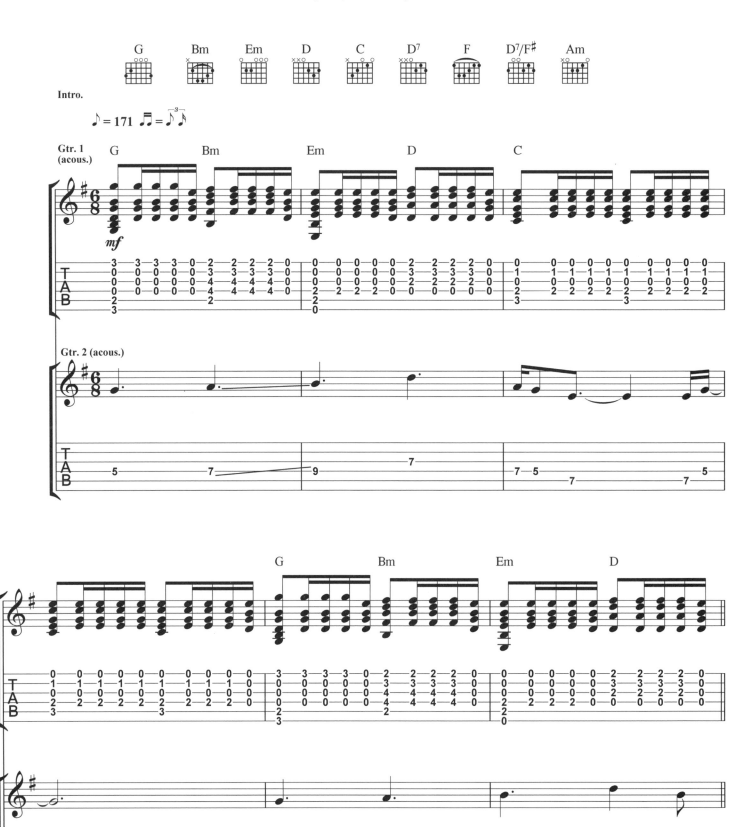

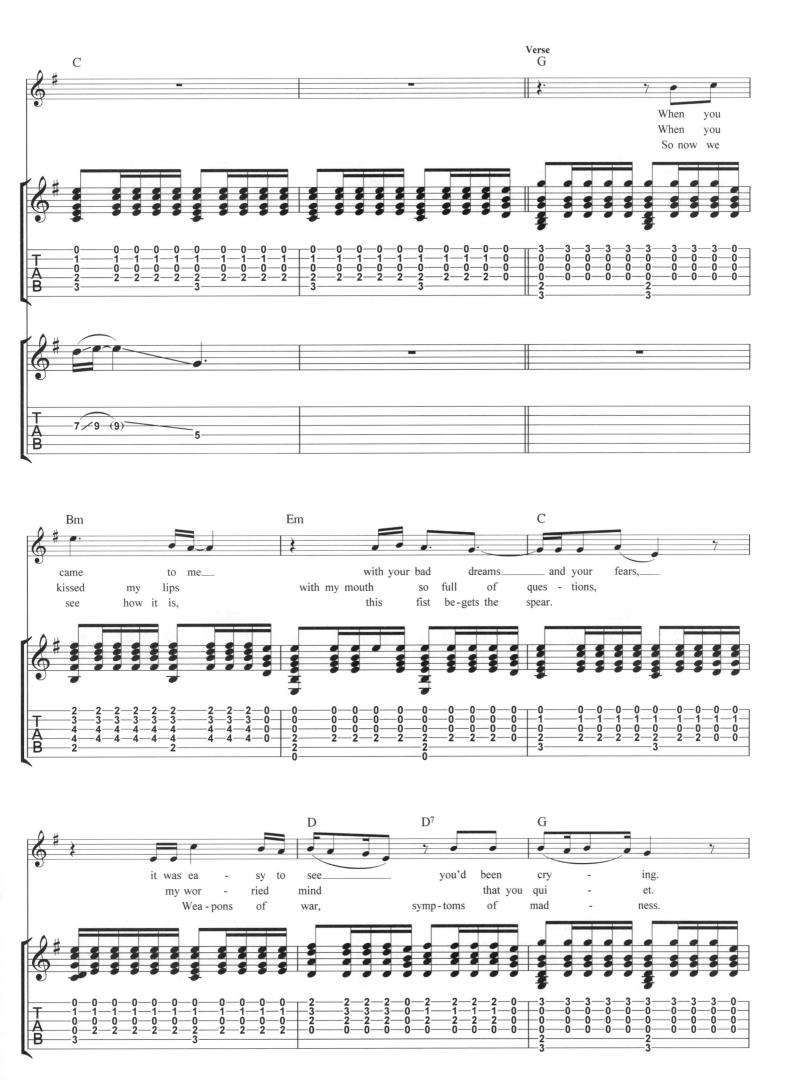

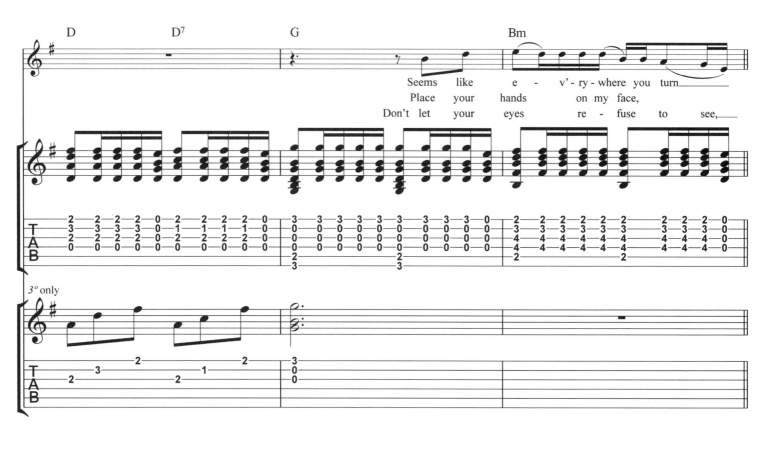

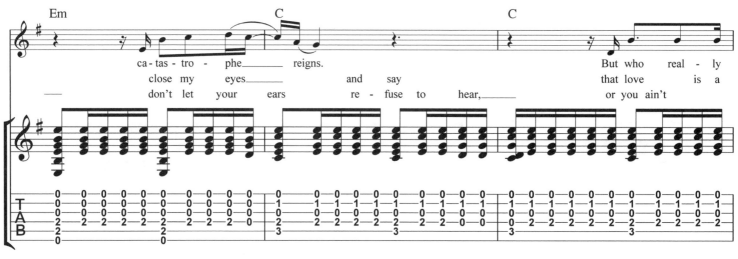

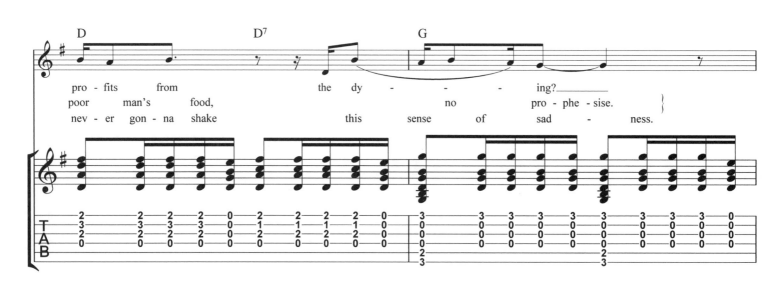

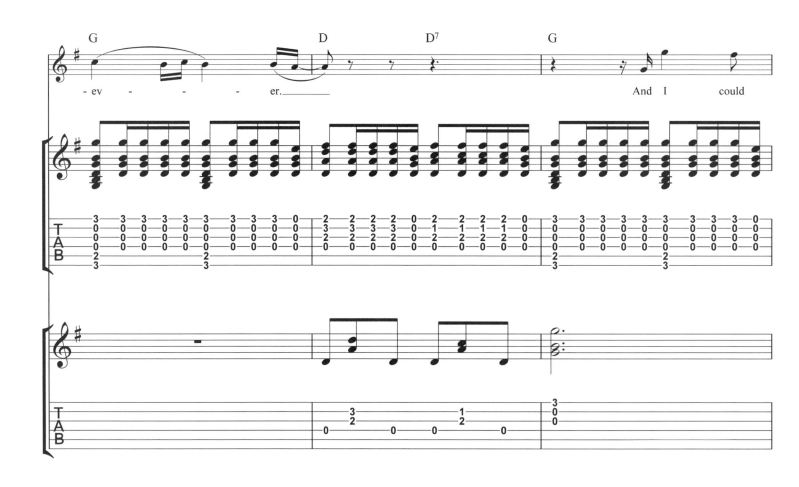

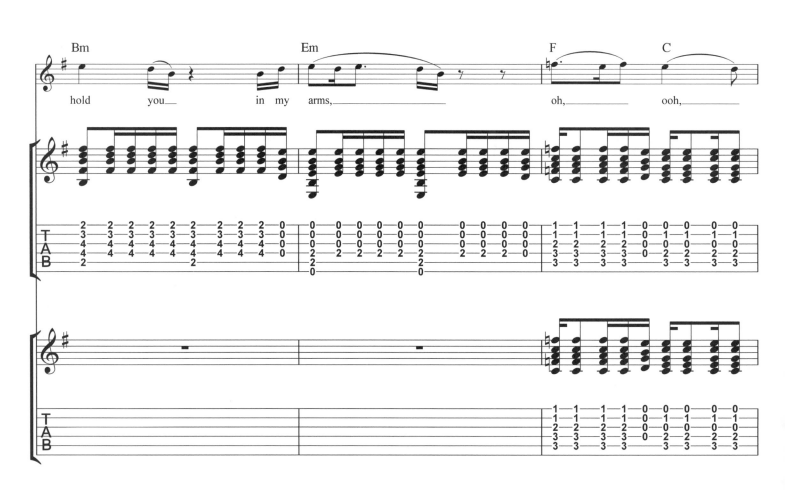

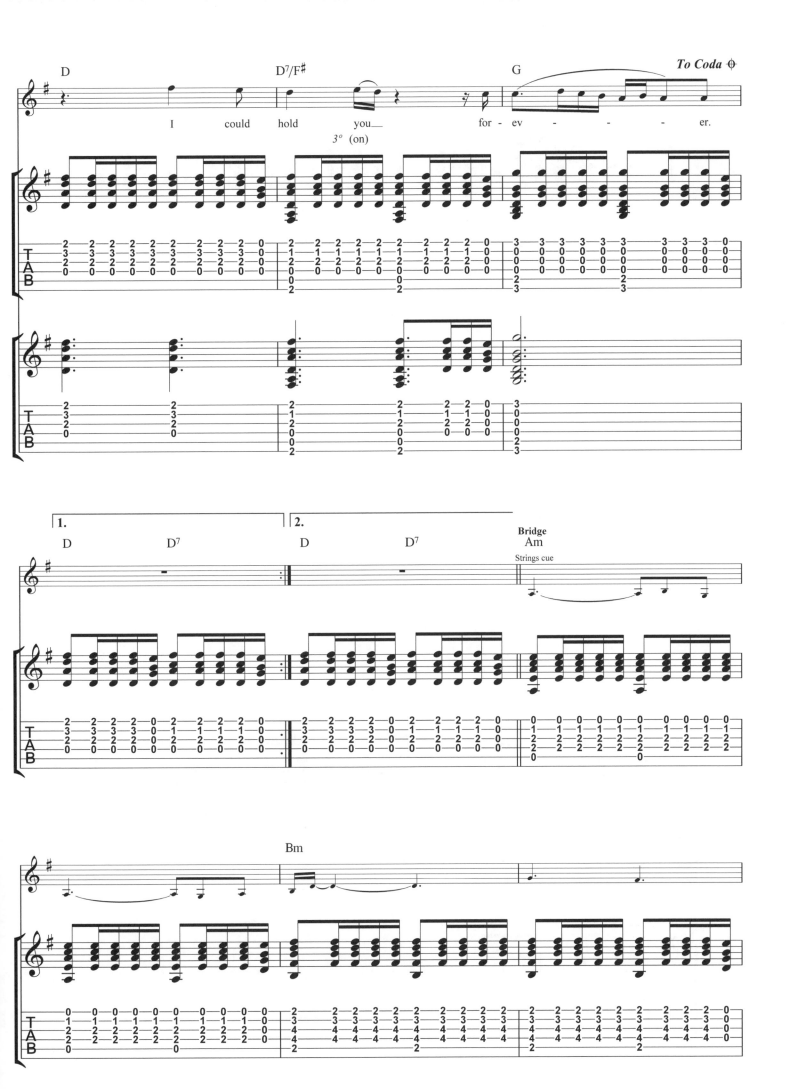

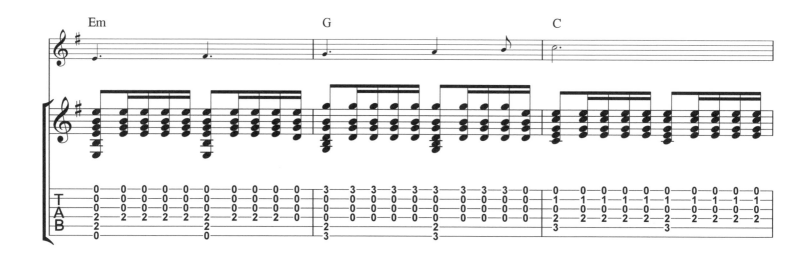

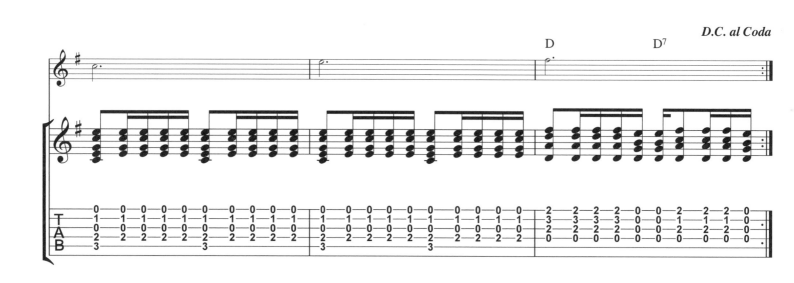

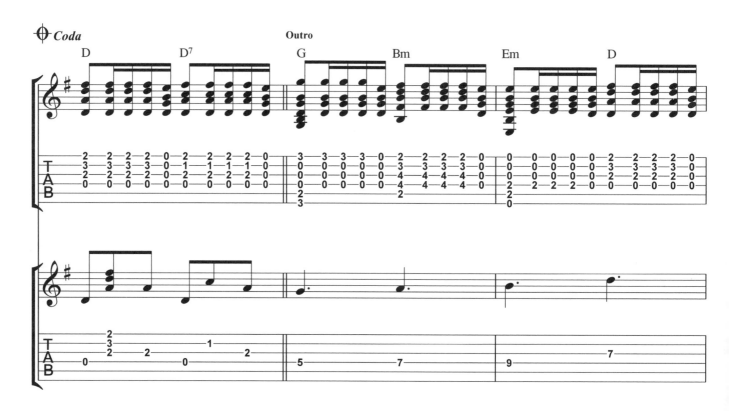

48

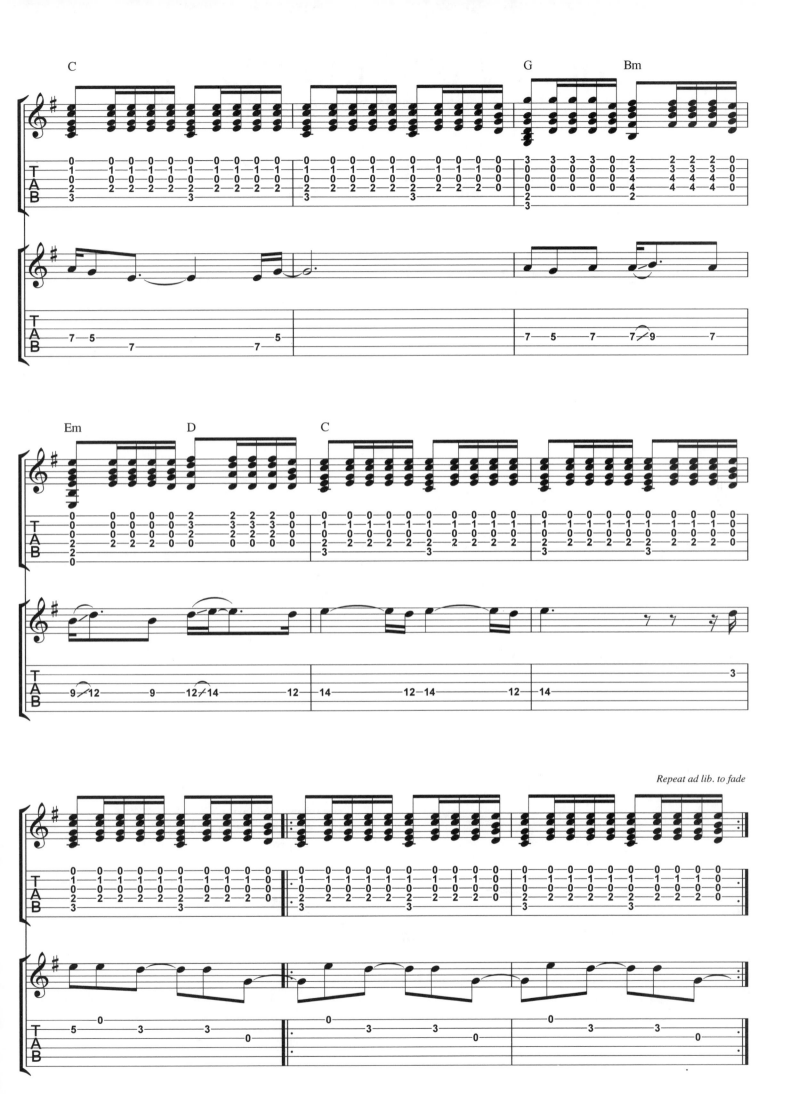

honey and the moon

Words & Music by Joseph Arthur

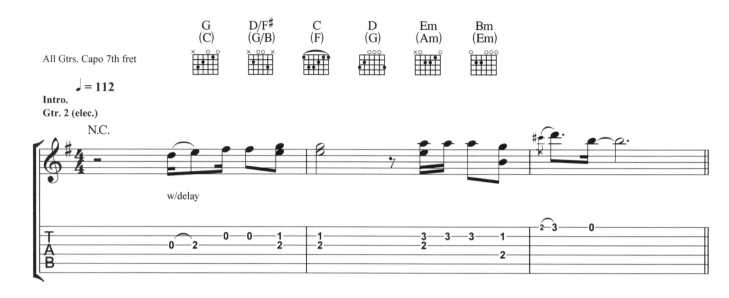

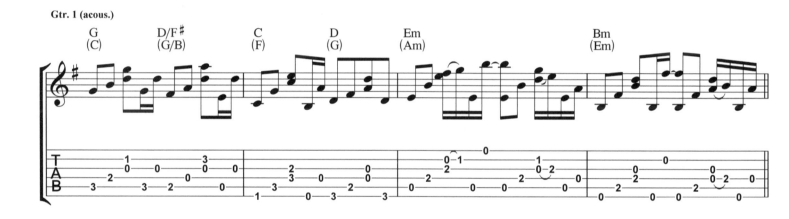

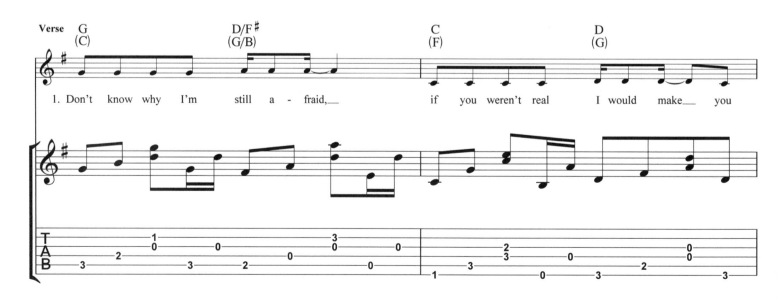

1. Don't know why I'm still a - fraid,___ if you weren't real I would make___ you

53

inaudible melodies

Words & Music by Jack Johnson

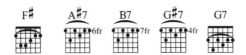

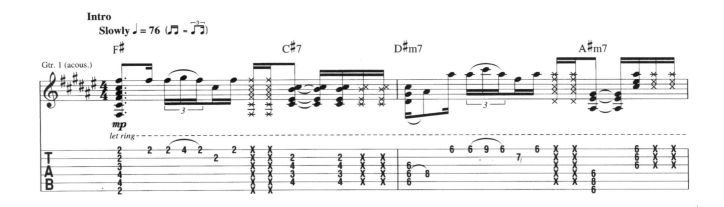

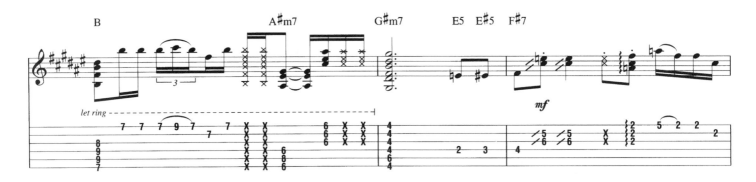

1. Brush - fire

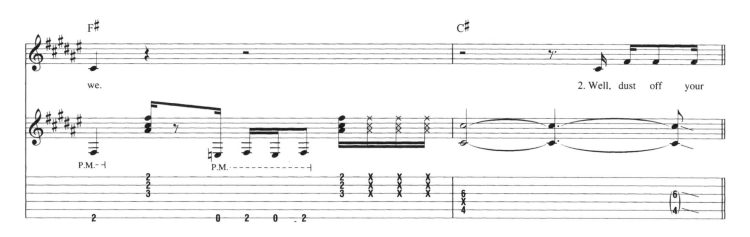

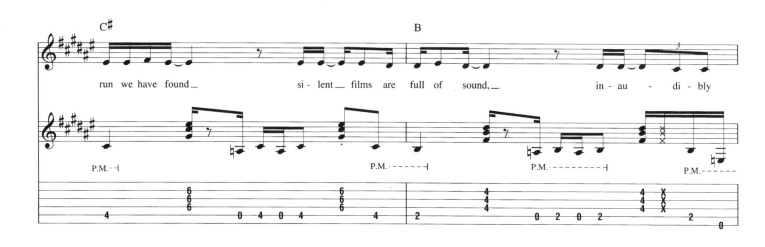

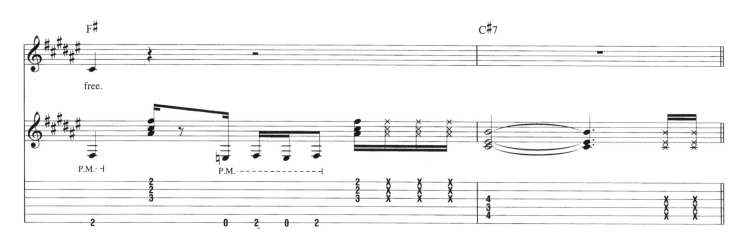

Chorus

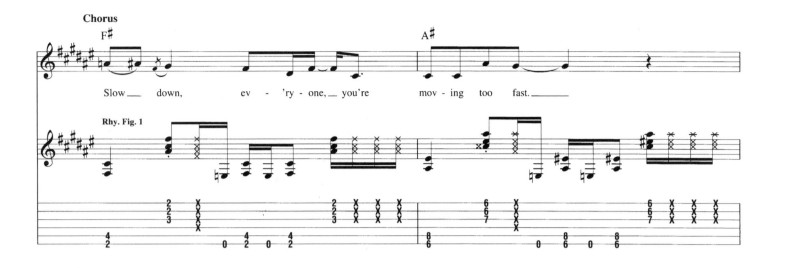

Slow down, ev - 'ry - one, you're mov - ing too fast.

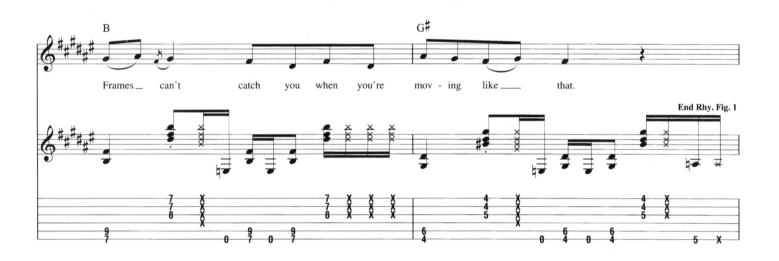

Frames can't catch you when you're mov - ing like that.

In - au - di - ble mel - o - dies serve nar - ra - tion - al strat - e - gies.

Un - ob - tru - sive tones help to no - tice noth - ing but the zone of

vi - su - al rel - e - van - cy. Frame - lines tell me what to see,

chop - ping like an axe or may - be Eis - en - stein should just re - lax.

Slow ____ down, ev - 'ry - one, ____ you're mov - ing too fast. ____

Frames ____ can't catch you when you're mov - ing like ____ that.

Guitar Solo

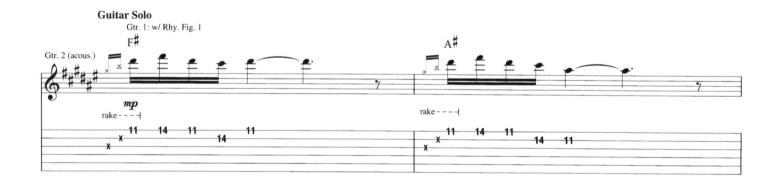

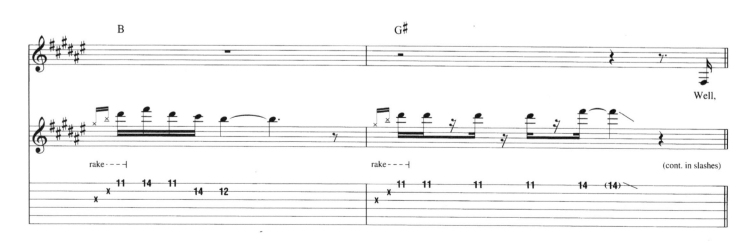

Well,

(cont. in slashes)

60

know-how

Words & Music by Eirik Bøe, Erlend Øye & Leslie Feist

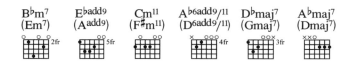

All guitars capo 6th fret

♩ = 160

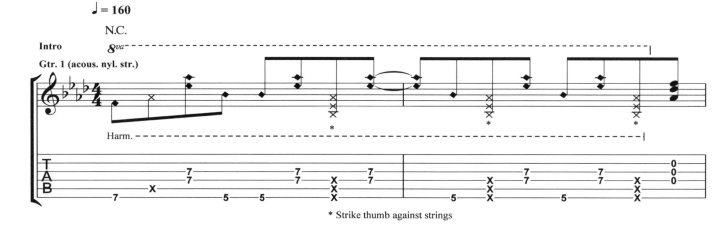

* Strike thumb against strings

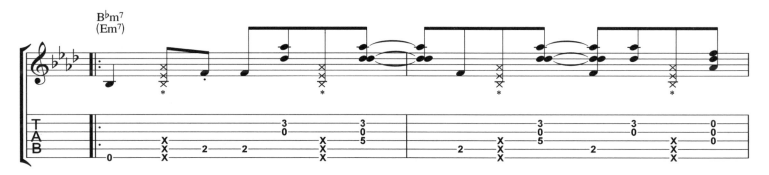

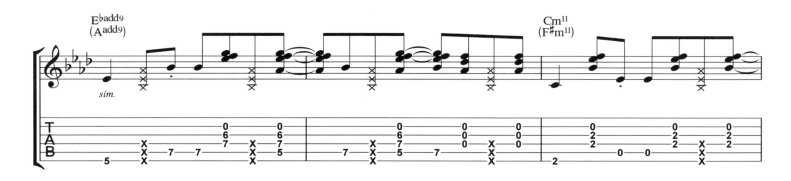

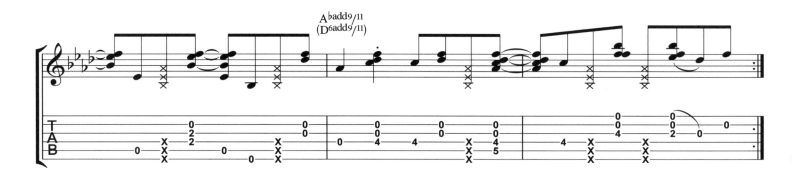

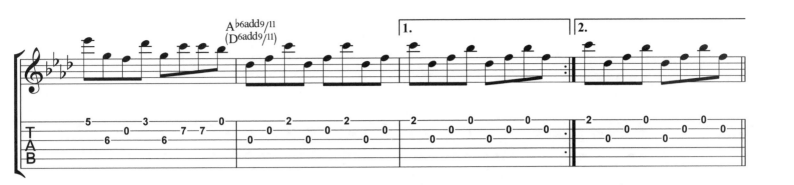

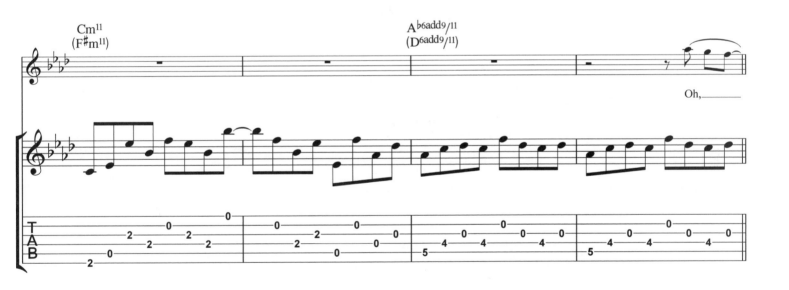

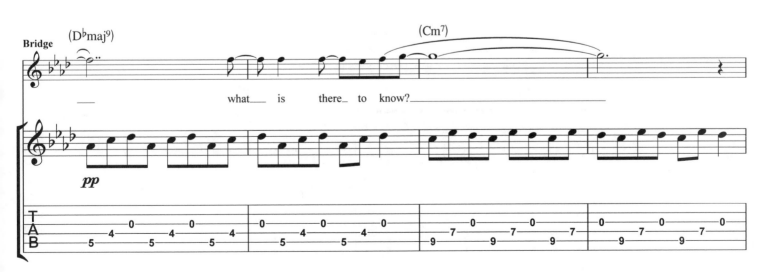

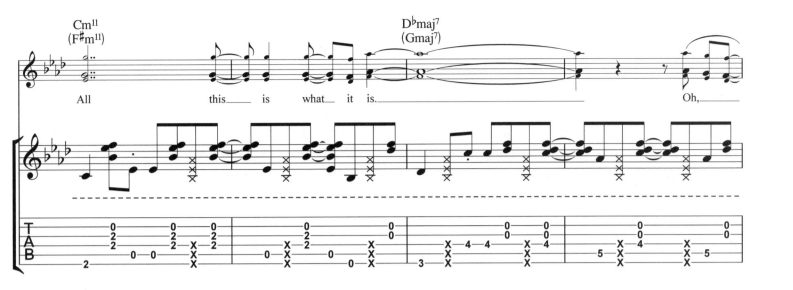

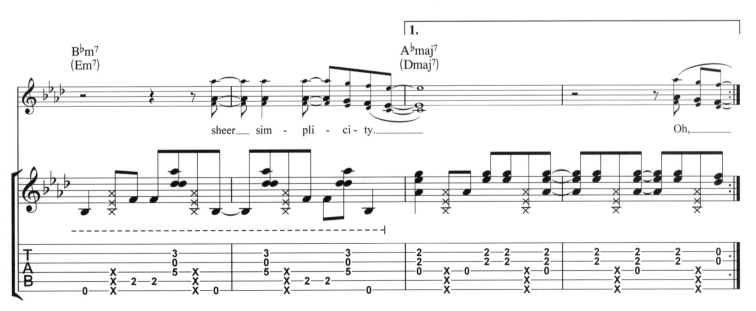

67

lost cause

Words & Music by Beck Hansen

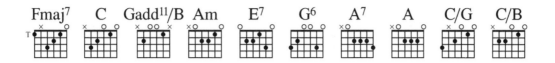

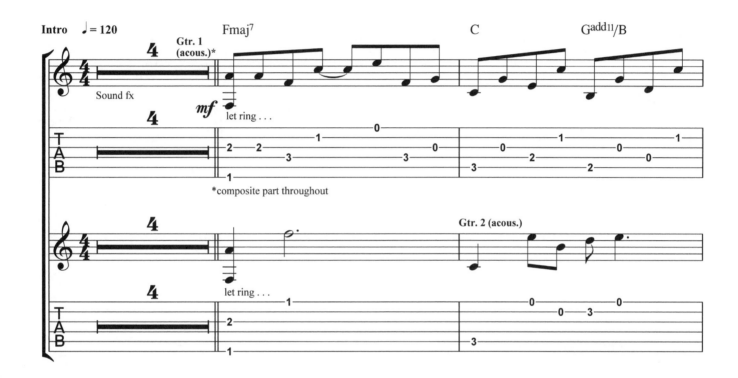

*composite part throughout

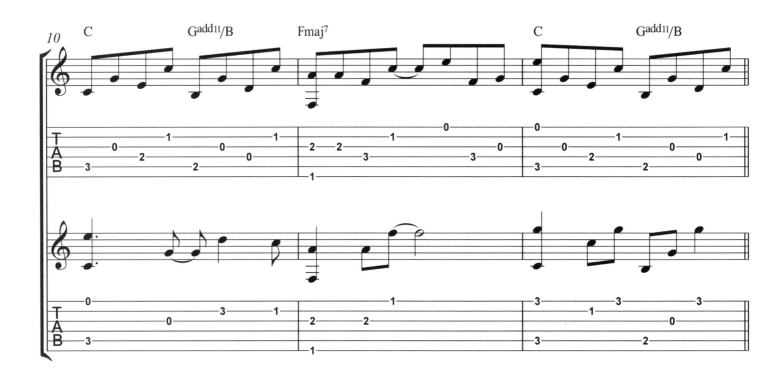

Verse

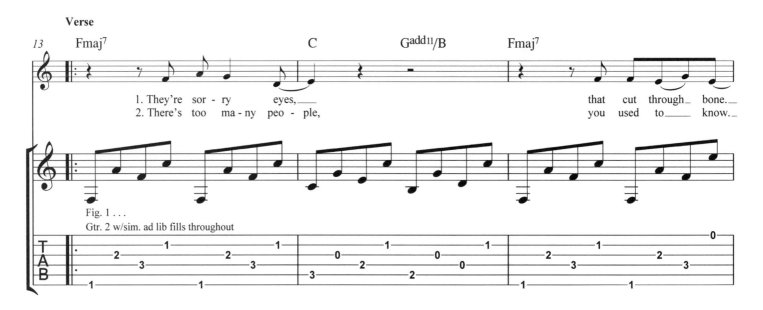

1. They're sor - ry eyes,___ that cut through___ bone.
2. There's too ma - ny peo - ple, you used to___ know.___

Fig. 1 . . .
Gtr. 2 w/sim. ad lib fills throughout

That make it hard,___
They see you com - ing,

71

mushaboom

Words & Music by Leslie Feist

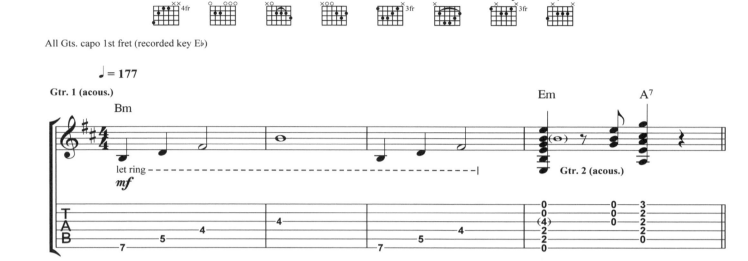

All Gts. capo 1st fret (recorded key E♭)

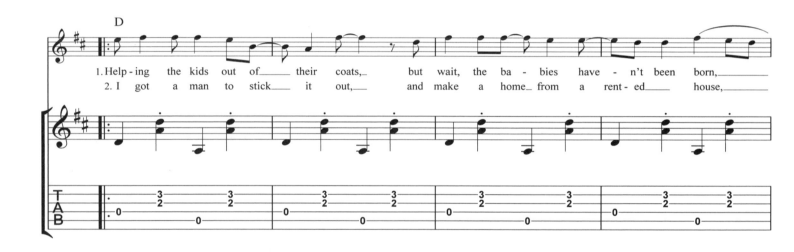

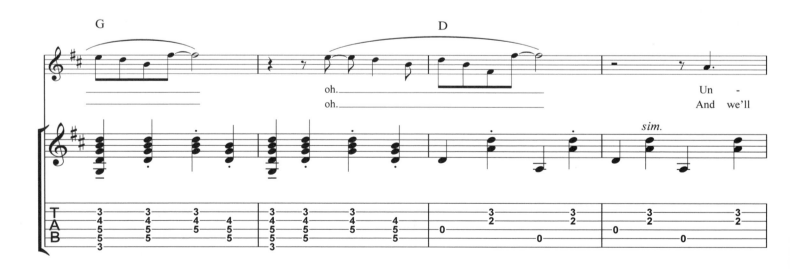

1. Help-ing the kids out of their coats, but wait, the ba-bies have-n't been born,
2. I got a man to stick it out, and make a home from a rent-ed house,

oh. Un-
oh. And we'll

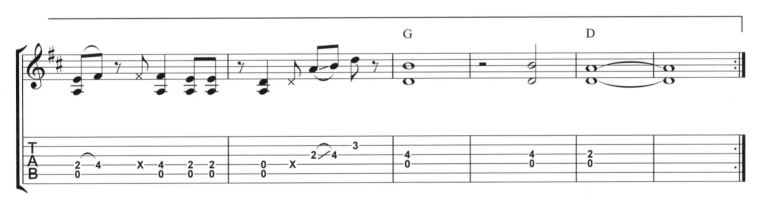

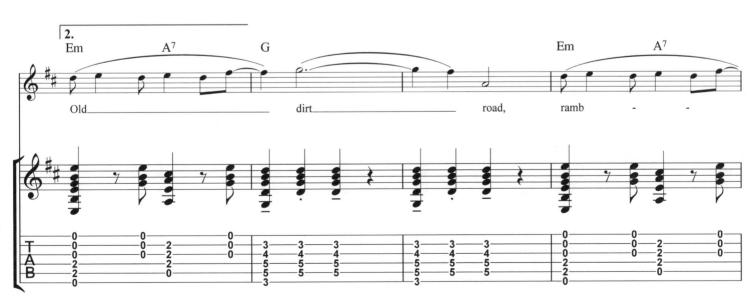

79

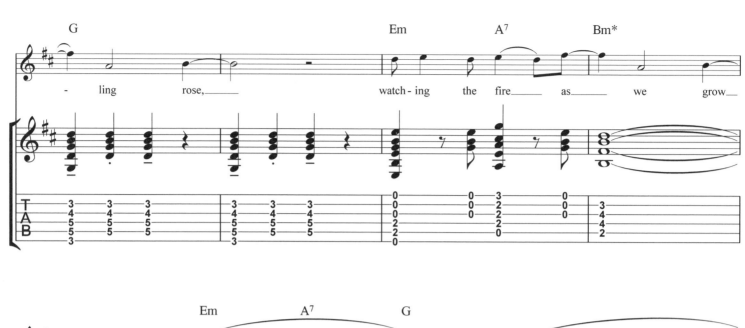

-ling rose,_____ watch-ing the fire_____ as_____ we grow

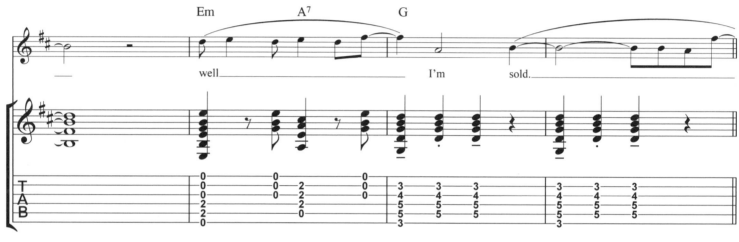

well_____ I'm sold.

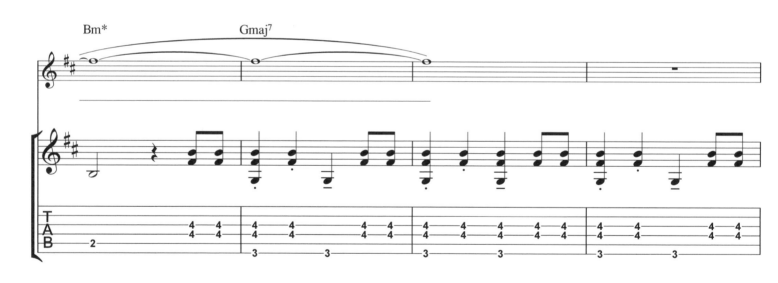

cont. ad lib. sim.

new slang

Words & Music by James Mercer

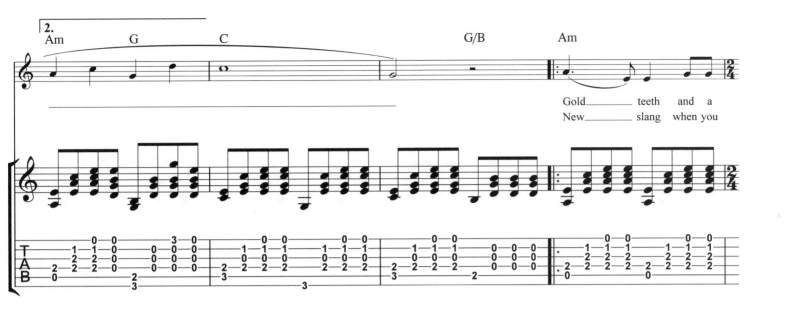

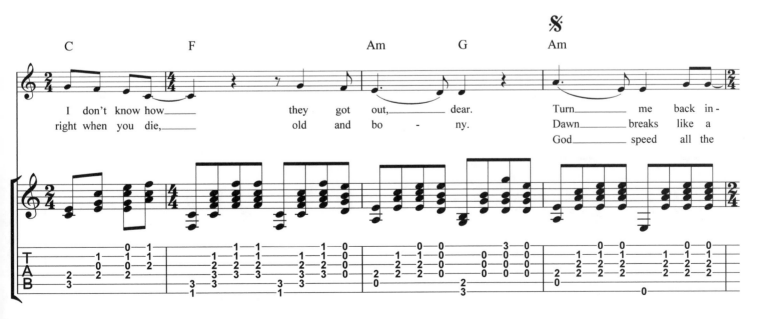

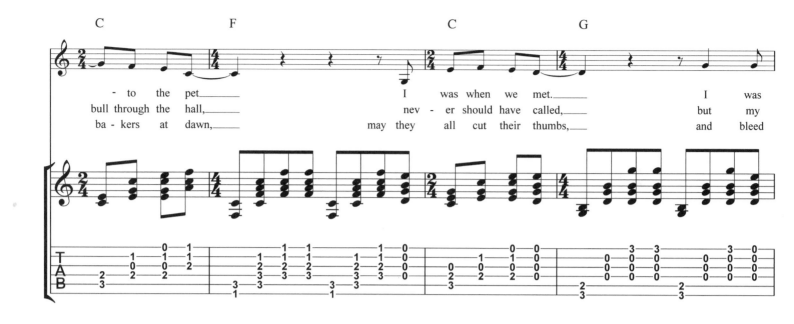

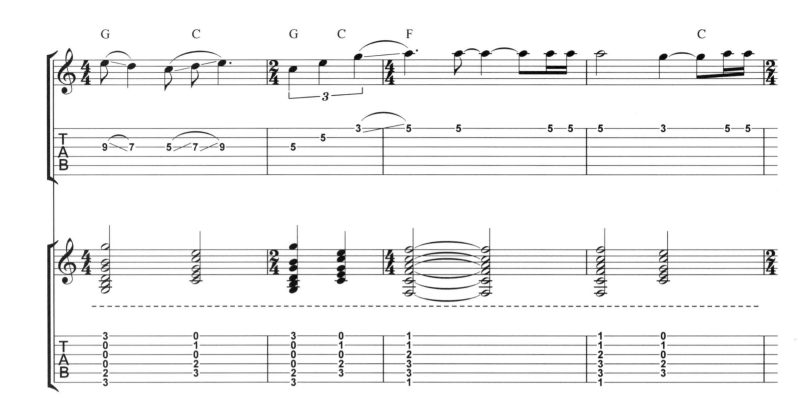

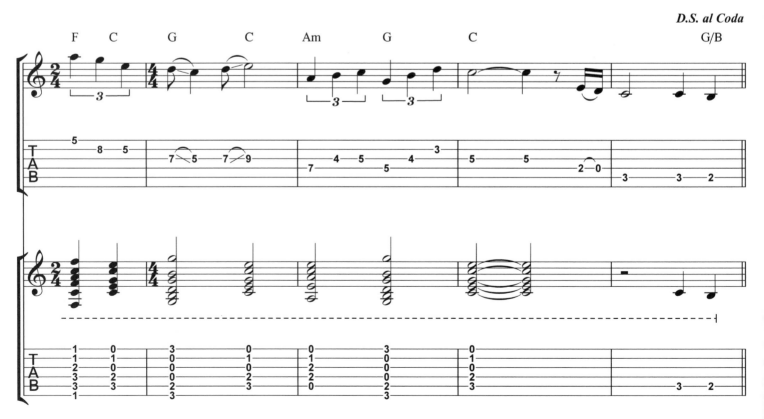

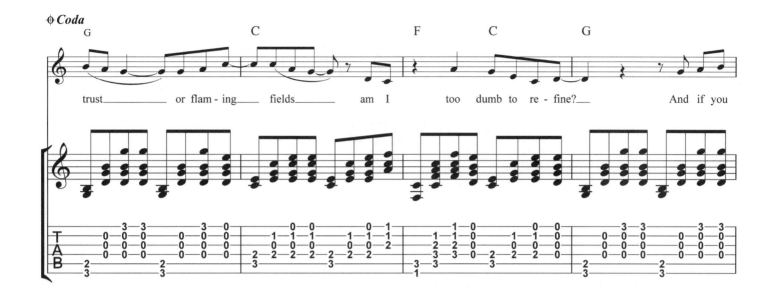

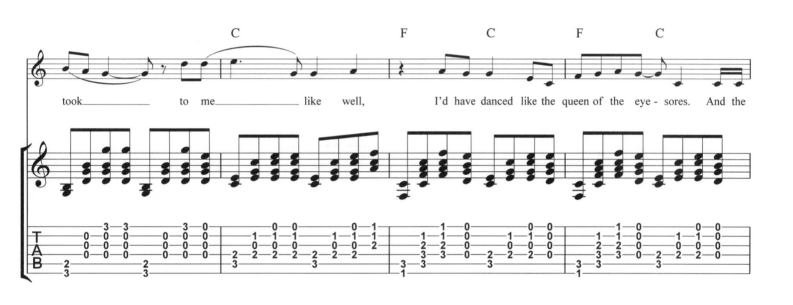

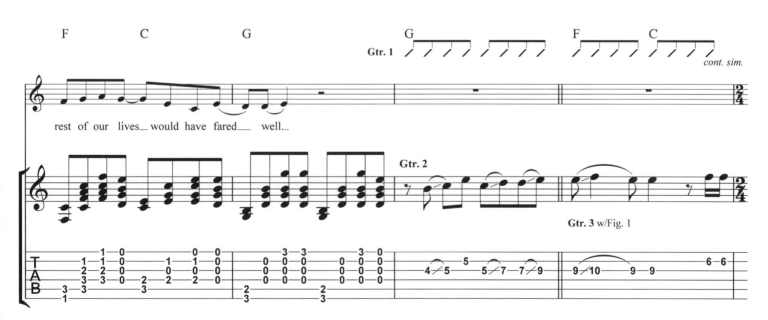

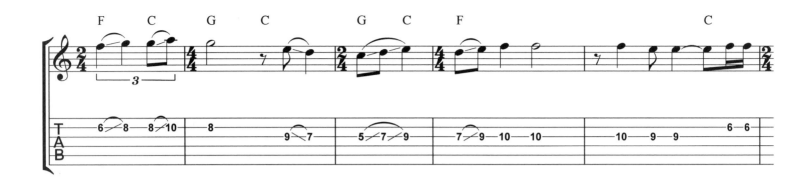

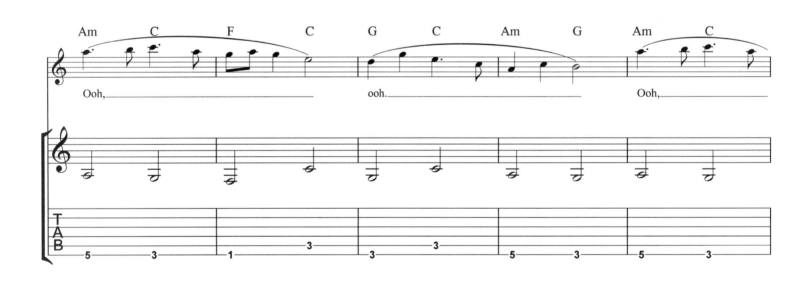

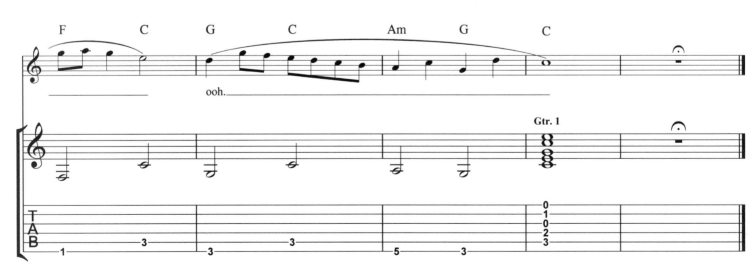

88

say yes

Words & Music by Elliott Smith

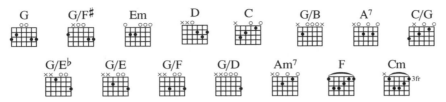

Tune all guitars down 1 tone. Original key (including vocals): F

1. I'm in love___ with the world___ through the eyes___ of a girl___
2. It's al-ways been___ wait and see,___ a hap-py day___ and then you pay,___

___ who's still a-round the morn-ing___ af-ter. We broke up___ a month a-go___
___ and feel like shit the morn-ing___ af-ter. But now I feel___ changed a-round

___ and I grew up___ I did-n't know___ I'd be a-round the morn-ing___ af-ter.
___ and in-stead of fall-ing down, I'm stand-ing up___ the morn-ing___ af-ter.

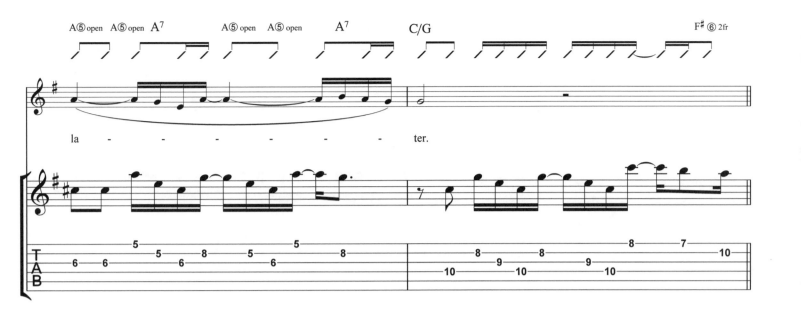

la - - - - - - ter.

And I could be___ a - no - ther fool___ or an ex - cep - tion to the rule,___

Gtr. 1 w/Fig. 1

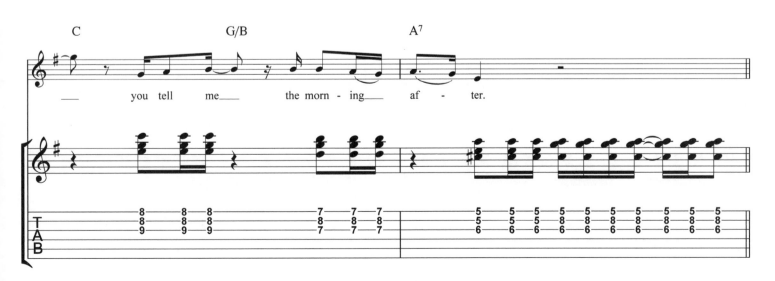

___ you tell me___ the morn - ing___ af - ter.

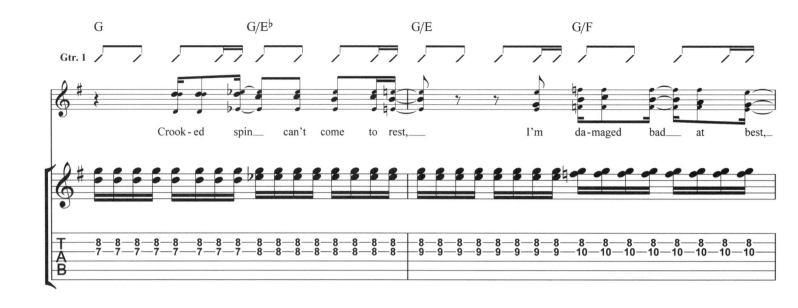

Crook - ed spin___ can't come to rest,___ I'm da-maged bad___ at best,___

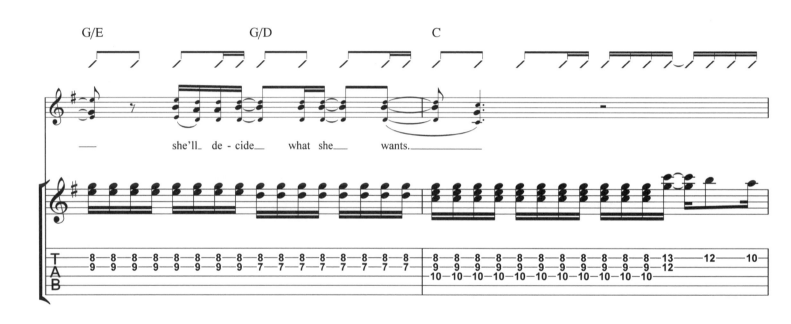

___ she'll de - cide___ what she___ wants.___

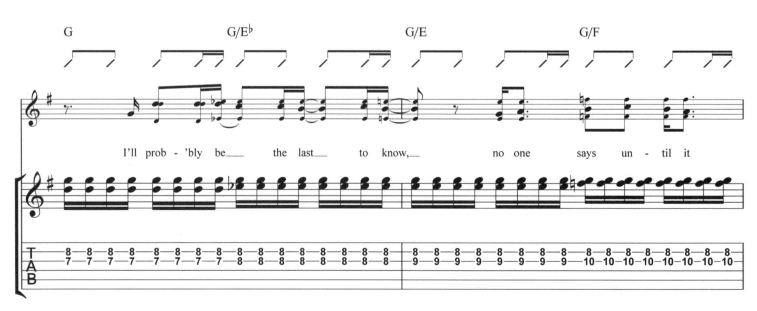

I'll prob - 'bly be___ the last___ to know, no one says un - til it

small world

Words & Music by Roddy Frame

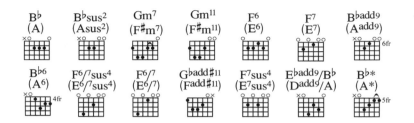

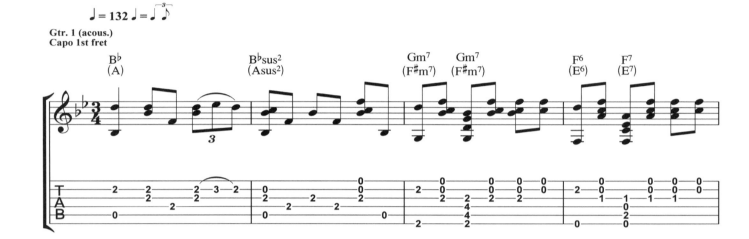

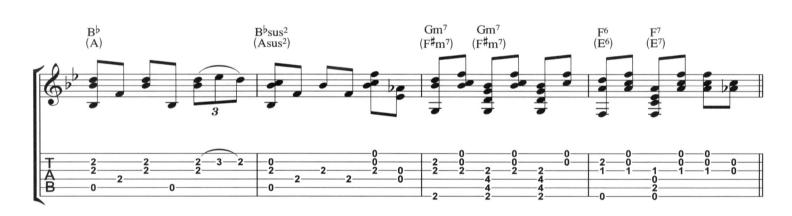

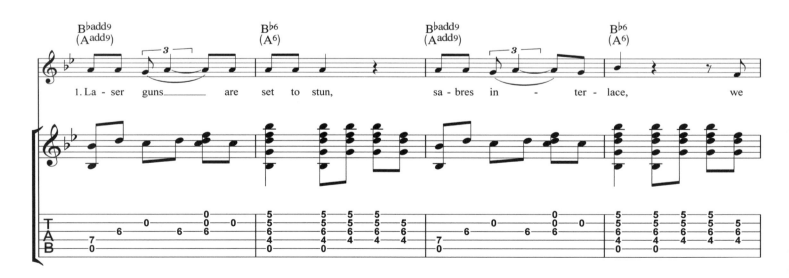

1. La - ser guns____ are set to stun, sa - bres in - ter - lace, we

crash - ing cars,_____ sun - burst gui - tars, am - phe - ta - mines_____ and_____ fame.___ And
clocks to whirl_____ and race, so my girl does_____ re - turn. And

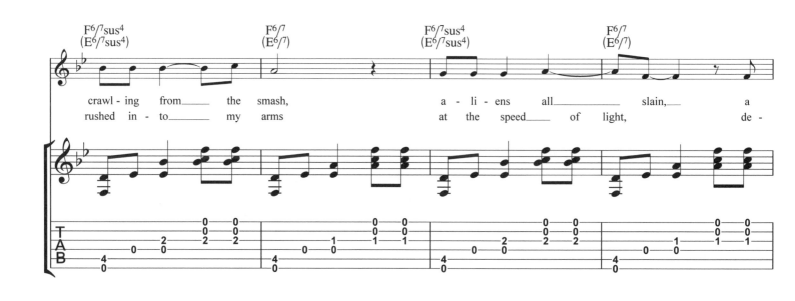

crawl - ing from_____ the smash, a - li - ens all_____ slain,_____ a
rushed in - to_____ my arms at the speed_____ of light, de -

beam of light in a flash lifts you up to where you know that you can choose to
- li - vered safe_____ from harm. Know - ing that you'll nev - er

96

we flew blind

Words & Music by James Yorkston

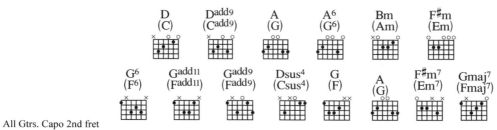

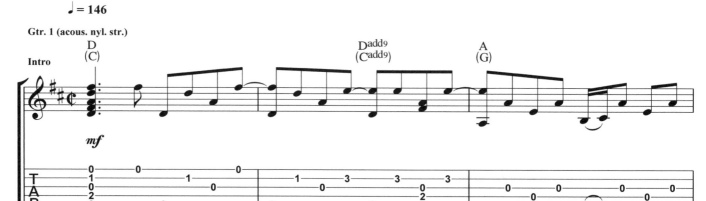

All Gtrs. Capo 2nd fret

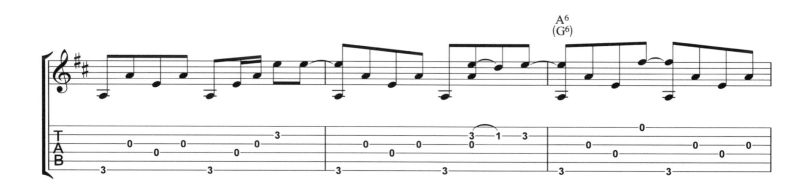

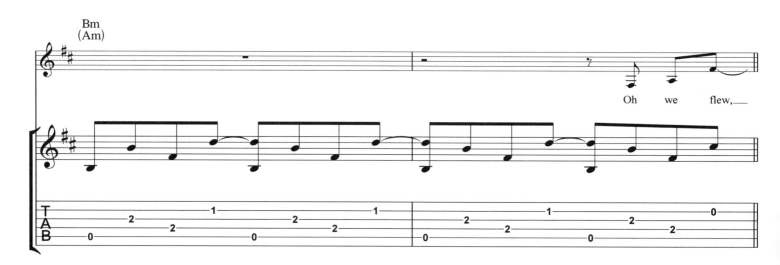

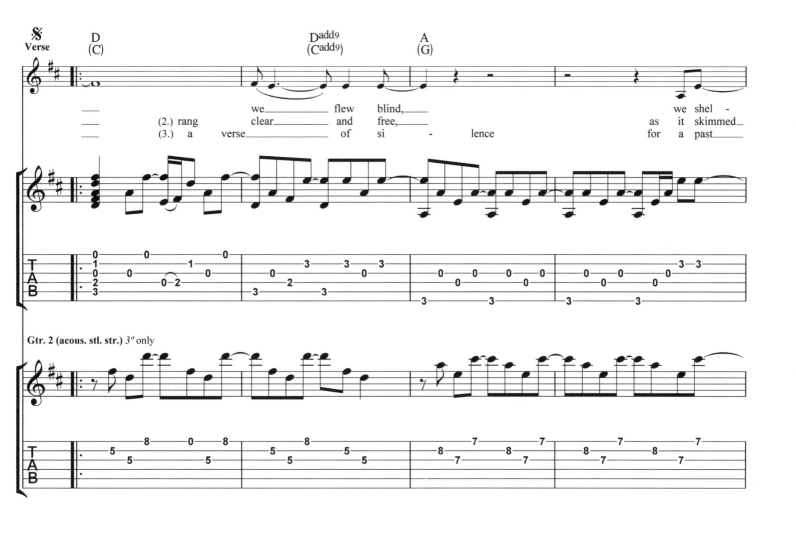

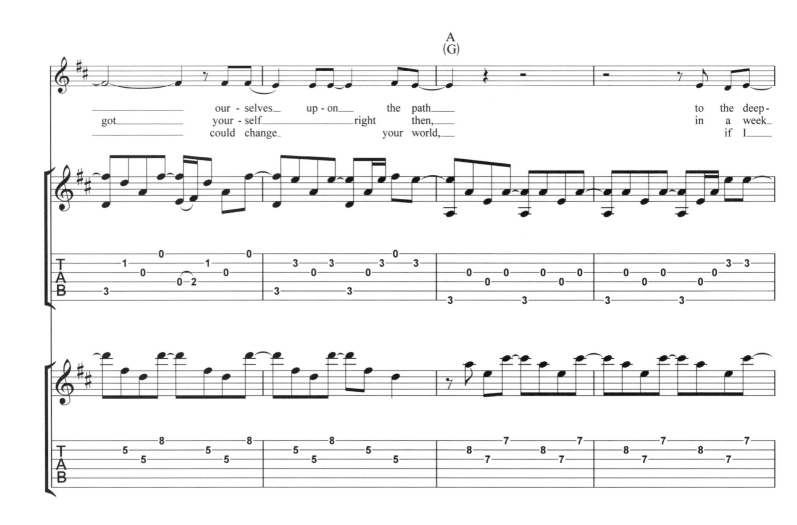

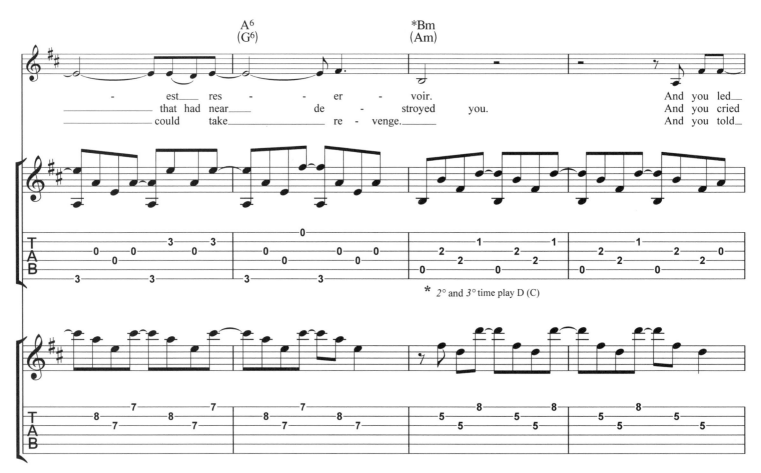

* *2° and 3° time play D (C)*

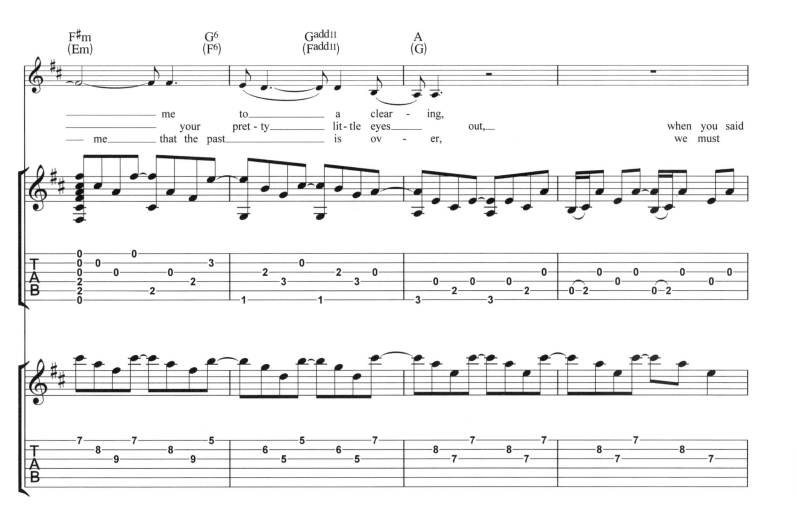

me to a clear - ing, your pret - ty lit - tle eyes out, me that the past is ov - er, when you said we must

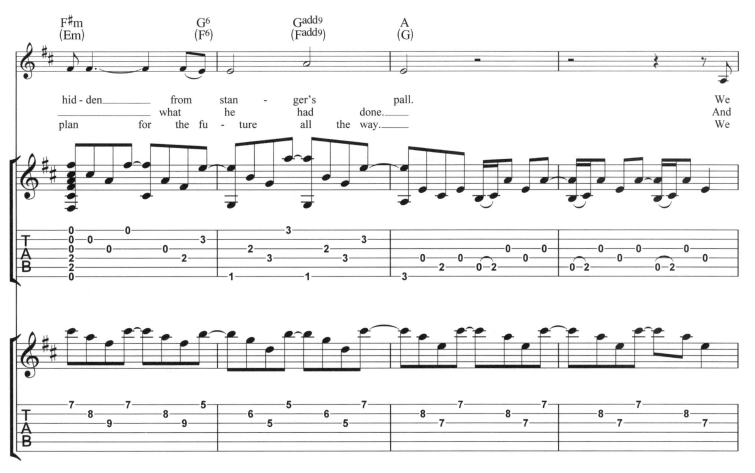

hid - den from stan - ger's pall. We
what he had done. And
plan for the fu - ture all the way. We

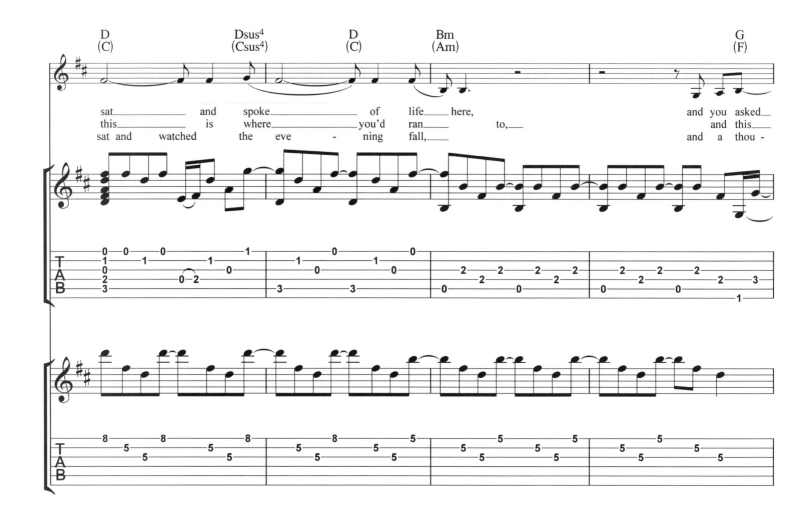

sat _____ and spoke _____ of life ___ here,
this _____ is where _____ you'd ran ___ to, ___
sat and watched the eve - ning fall, ___

and you asked ___
and this ___
and a thou -

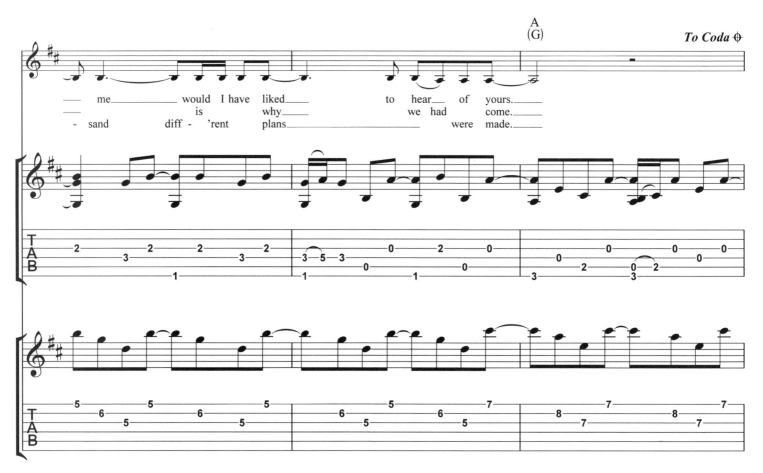

— me ___ would I have liked ___ to hear ___ of yours. ___
— is why ___ we had come. ___
- sand diff - 'rent plans ___ were made.

To Coda ⊕

And your voice‗

Interlude

And I sang_

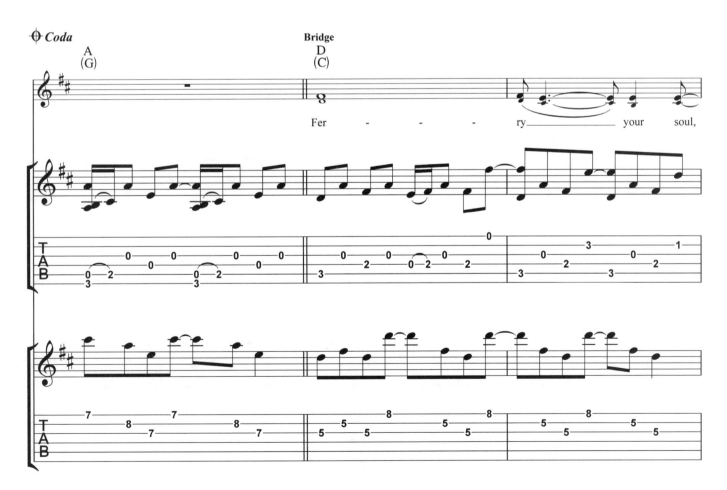

Fer - - - ry_____ your soul,

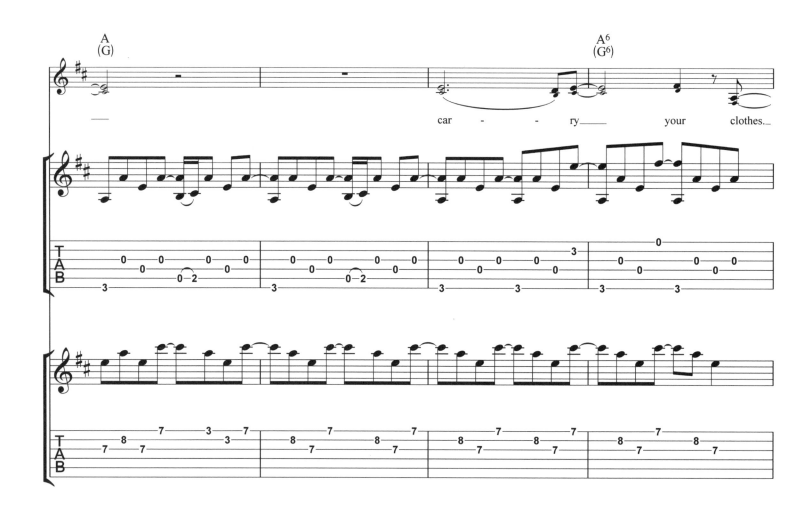

car - - ry___ your clothes.___

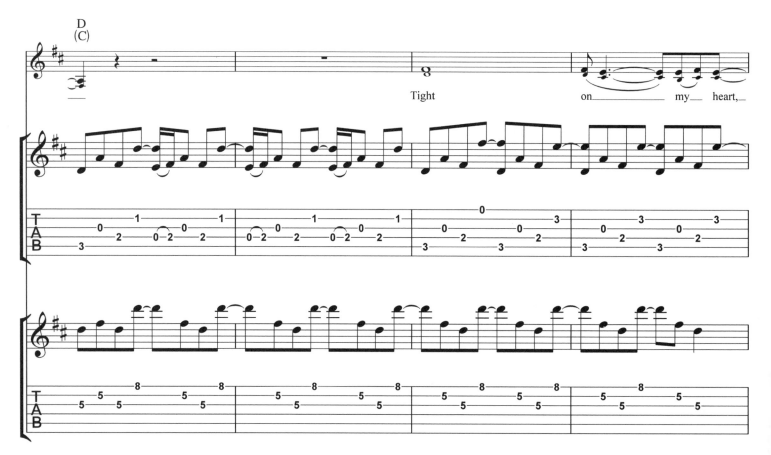

Tight on_____ my___ heart,___

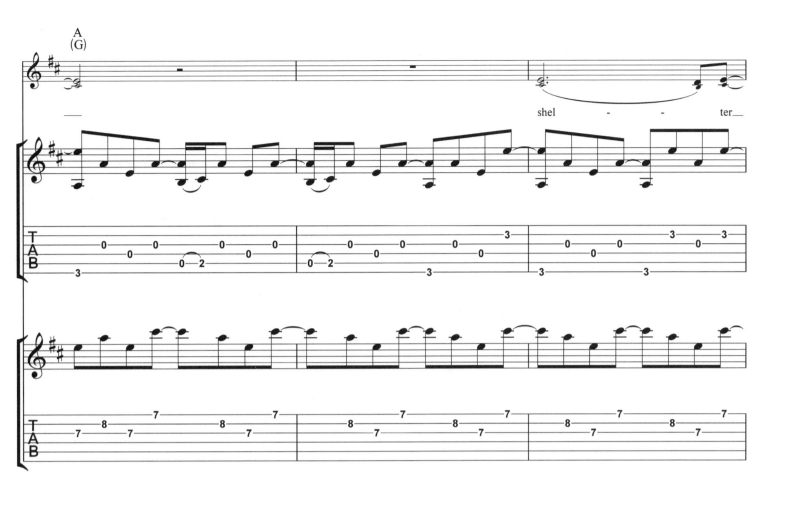

shel - - ter

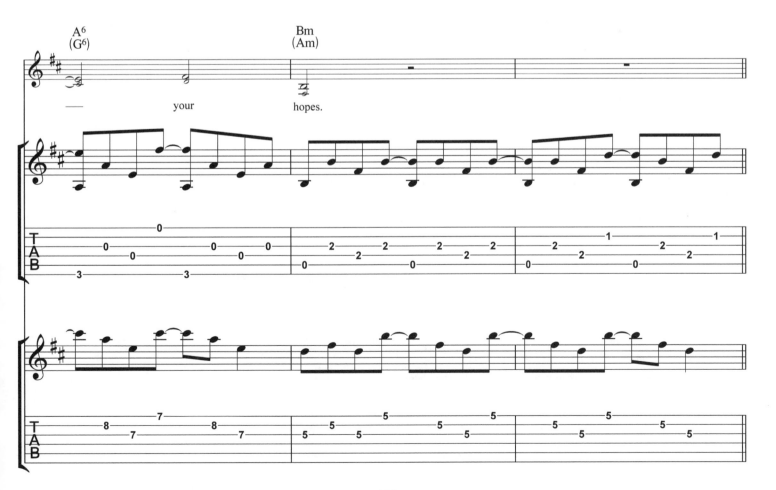

your hopes.

109

wild flowers

Words & Music by Ryan Adams

113

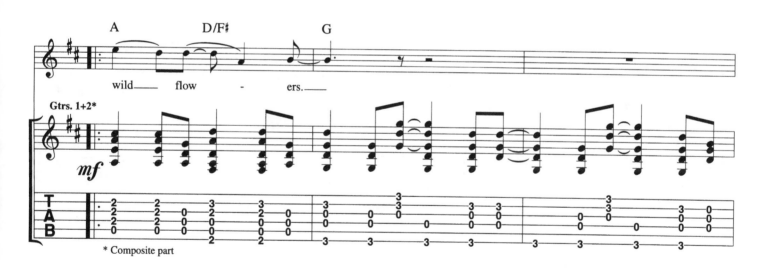

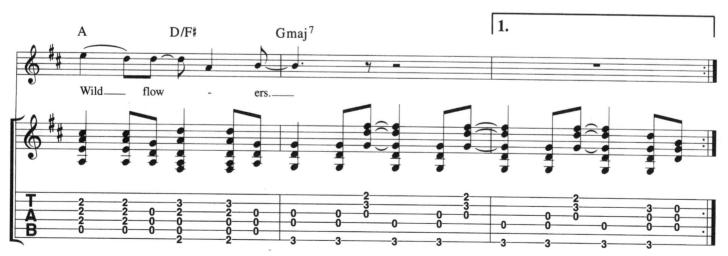

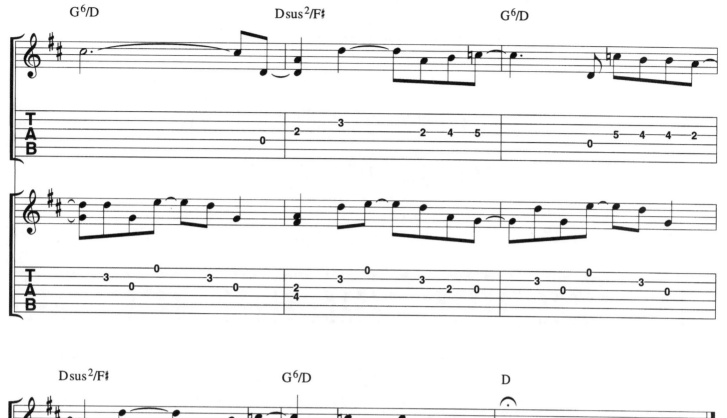

Verse 2:

Poor girl
Lonely, shuffles through the parade
Of a sleepless circus promenade
Hold on dear.

Poor girl, no Ma
Sister steals her a coat
For the windless breezes
Sleep now and Jesus will come, dear.

til kingdom come

Words & Music by
Guy Berryman, Jon Buckland, Will Champion & Chris Martin

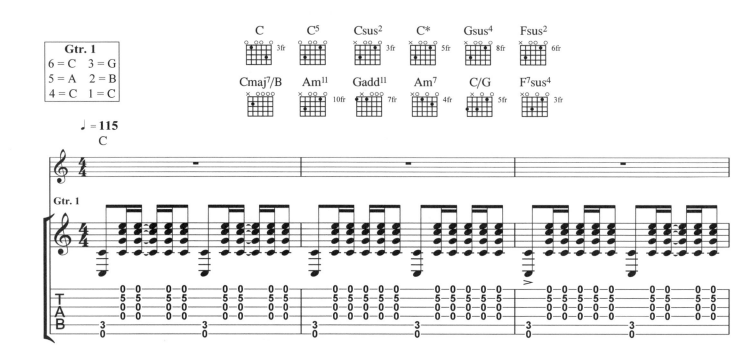

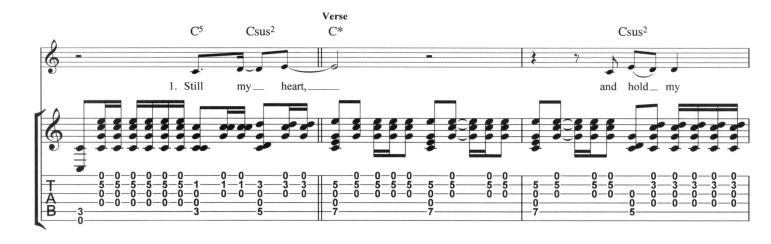

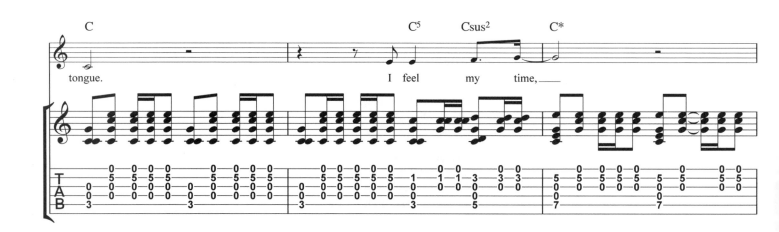

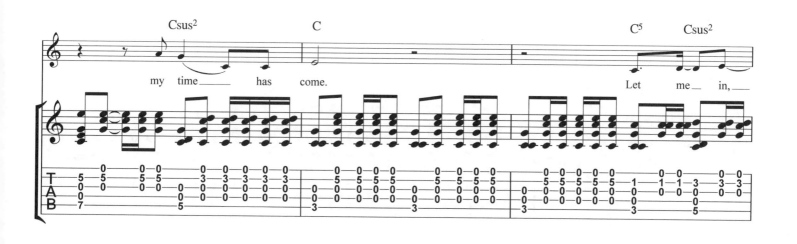

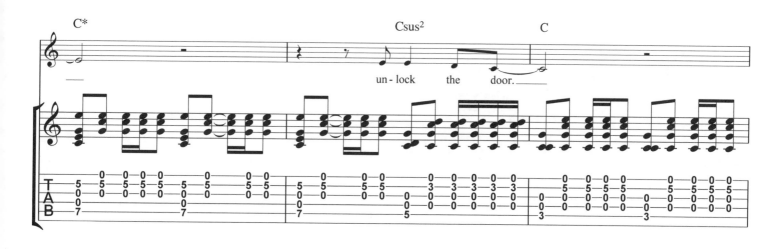

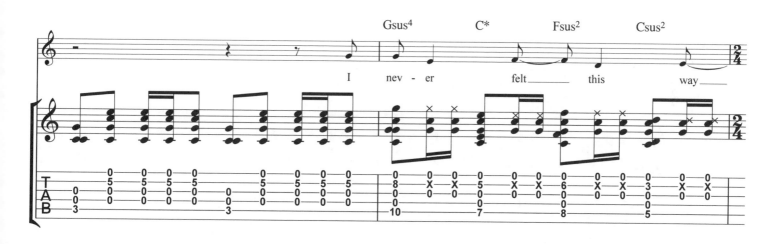

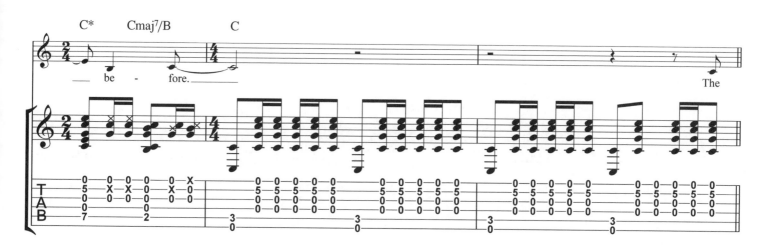

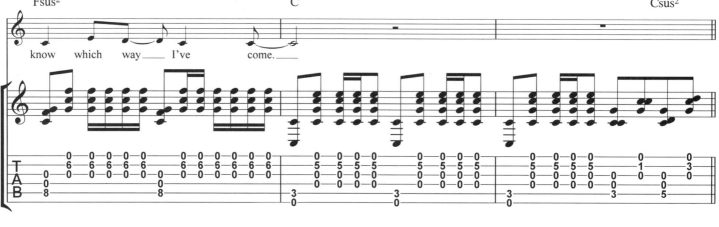

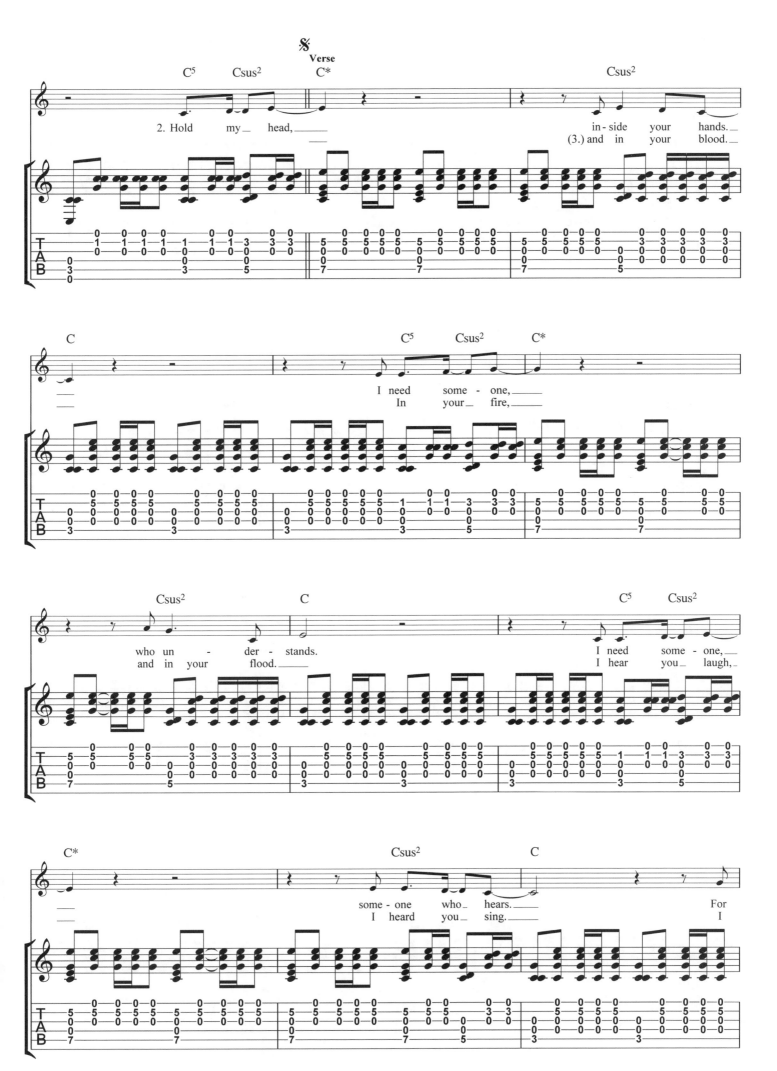

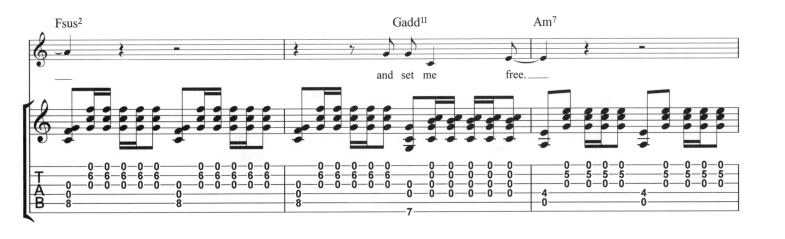

and set me free.___

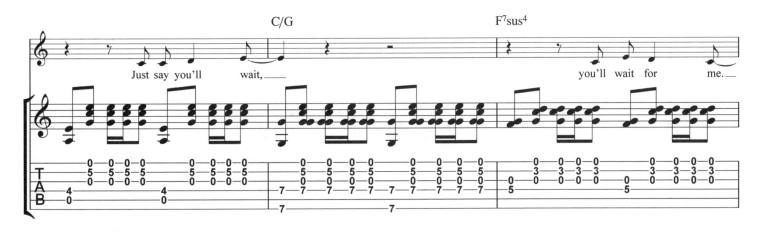

Just say you'll wait,___ you'll wait for me.___

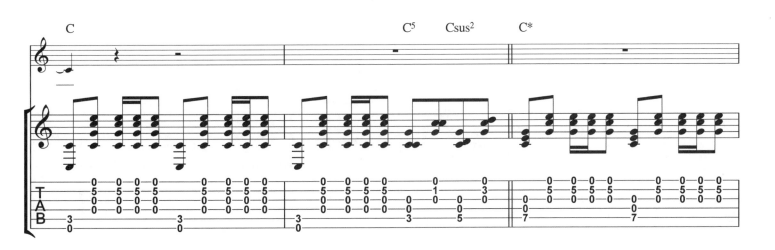

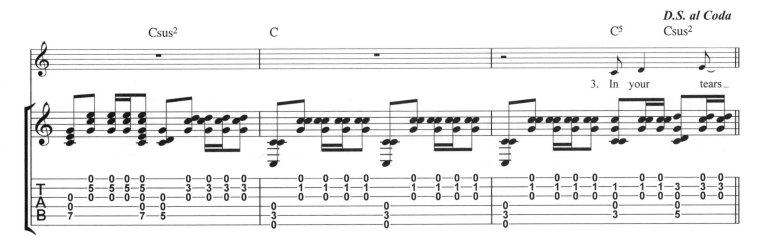

3. In your tears___

125

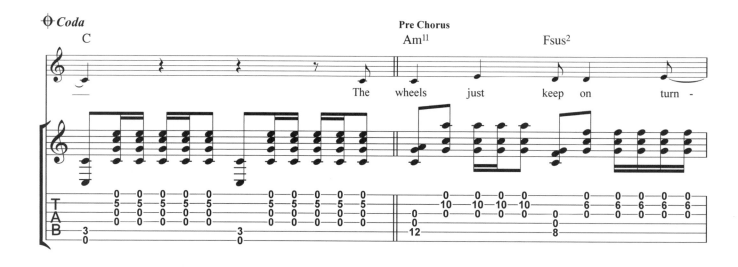

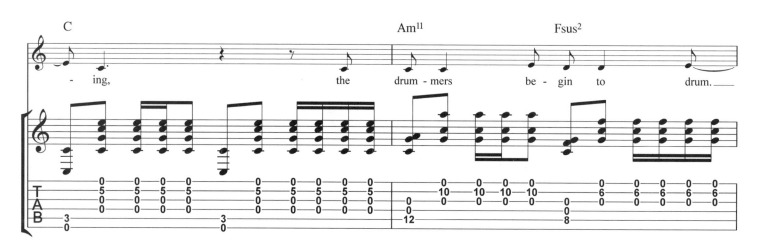

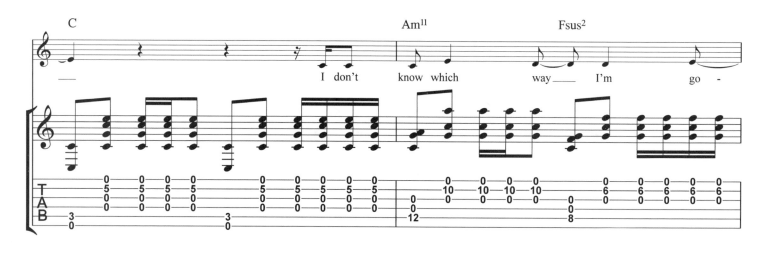

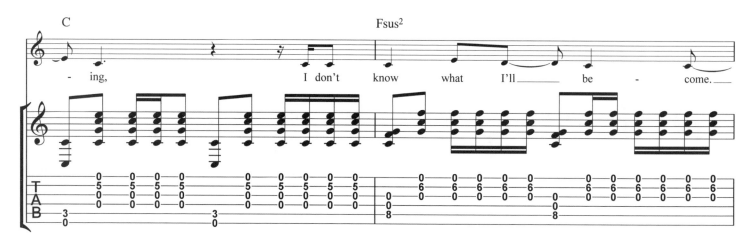

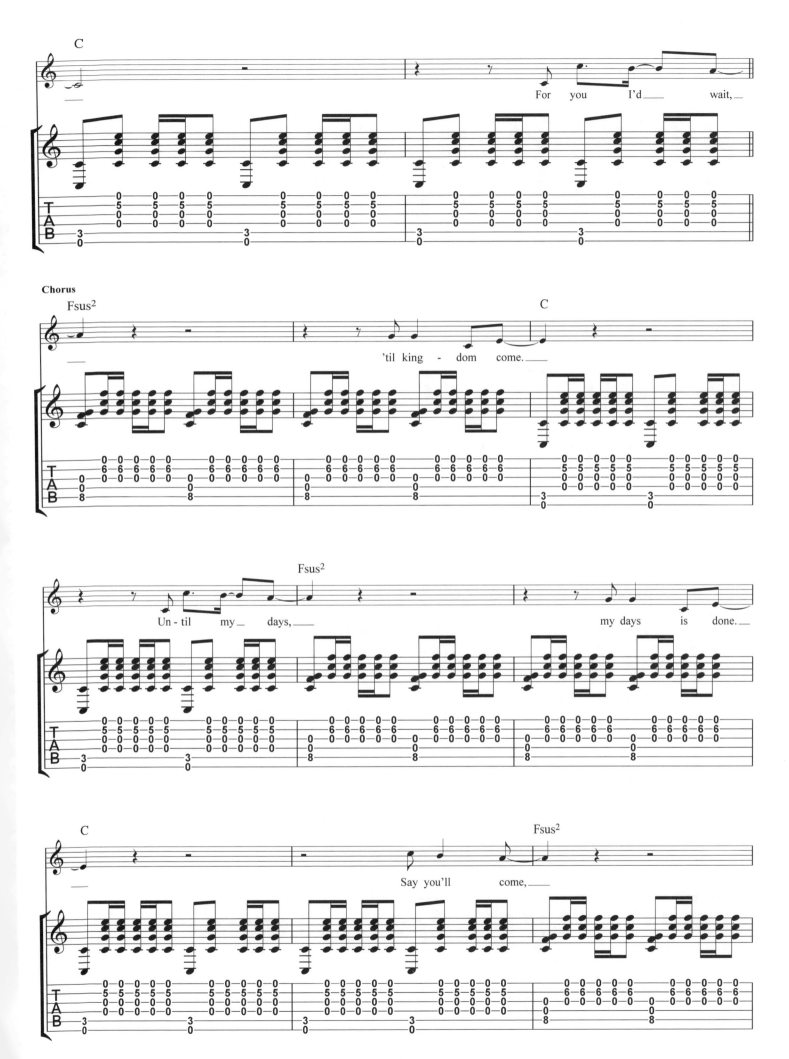

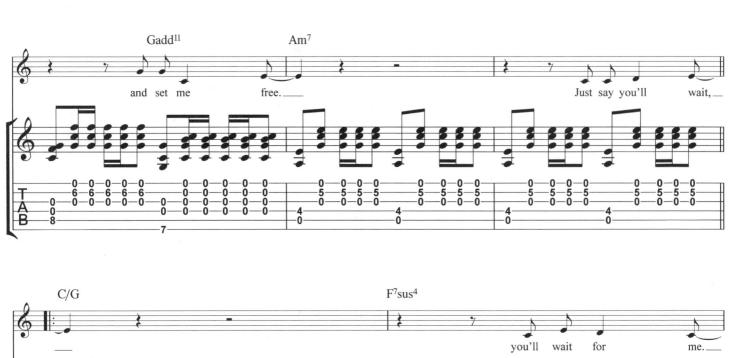

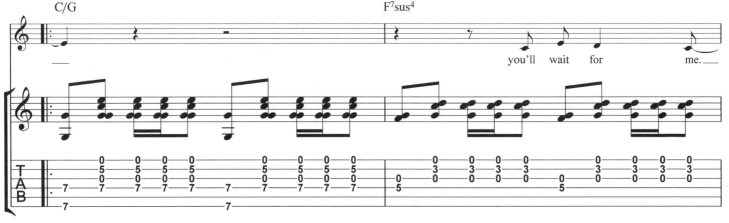

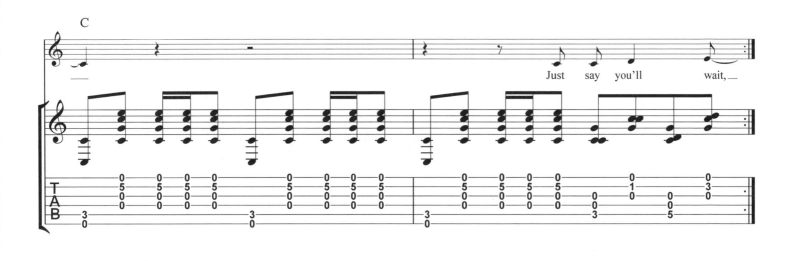

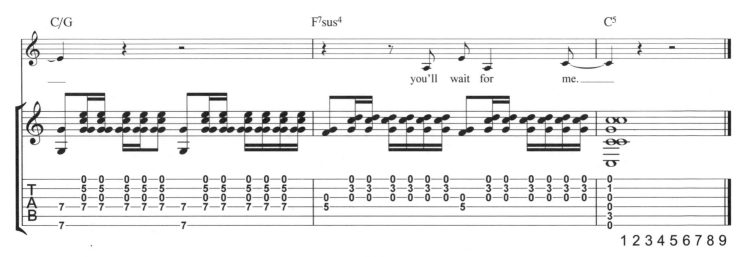

1 2 3 4 5 6 7 8 9